ARDUINO PROJECTS BOOK

ARDUINO - THE PROJECTS BOOK

AUTHORS
Projects and text by Scott Fitzgerald and Michael Shiloh.
Additional text review by Tom Igoe

DESIGN AND ART DIRECTION
TODO
Giorgio Olivero, Vanessa Poli, Michelle Nebiolo, Stefania Vulpi
todo.to.it

DIGITAL FABRICATION AND PROJECT MANAGEMENT
Officine Arduino Torino, Katia De Coi, Enrico Bassi, Stefano Paradiso,
Andrea Richetta

ADVISORS AND SUPPORTERS
Massimo Banzi

PROJECT TESTERS AND PROOFREADERS
Michael Shiloh, Michelle Nebiolo, Katia De Coi, Alessandro Buat,
Federico Vanzati, David Mellis, Arturo Guadalupi, Luisa Castiglioni

THANKS
Big thanks to the entire user community for their continued
contributions, support, and feedback. Special thanks to the
Fritzing team: some of the electronic components illustrations
used in the book are taken or modified from the open-source
Fritzing project (www.fritzing.org).
Heartfelt thanks to Paul Badger for the CapacitiveSensor library
used in Project 13.

THANKS FOR THE FIRST EDITION
Mario Ciardulli, Gianluca Martino

INDEX

4	00	INTRODUCTION
20	01	Get to Know Your Tools
32	02	Spaceship Interface
42	03	Love-o-Meter
52	04	Color Mixing Lamp
62	05	Mood Cue
70	06	Light Theremin
78	07	Keyboard Instrument
86	08	Digital Hourglass
94	09	Motorized Pinwheel
102	10	Zoetrope
114	11	Crystal Ball
124	12	Knock Lock
136	13	Touchy-feely Lamp
144	14	Tweak the Arduino Logo
156	15	Hacking Buttons
162	A/Z	GLOSSARY

00

Everyone, every day, uses technology. Most of us leave the programming to engineers because we think coding and electronics are complicated and difficult; actually, they can be fun and exciting activities. Thanks to Arduino, designers, artists, hobbyists and students of all ages are learning to create things that light up, move, and respond to people, animals, plants, and the rest of the world.

Over the years Arduino has been used as the "brain" in thousands of projects, one more creative than the last. A worldwide community of makers has gathered around this open-source platform, moving from personal computing to personal fabrication, and contributing to a new world of participation, cooperation and sharing.

Arduino is open and simple. It's founded on lessons we've learned teaching our own classes: if you start with the assumption that learning to make digital technologies is simple and accessible, you can make it so. Suddenly electronics and code become creative tools that anyone can use – like brushes and paint. This book walks you through the basics in a hands-on way, with creative projects you build by learning. Once you've mastered the basics, you'll have a palette of software and circuits that you can use to create something beautiful, and make someone smile with what you invent.

WELCOME TO ARDUINO!

ARDUINO MAKES IT AS EASY AS POSSIBLE TO PROGRAM TINY COMPUTERS CALLED MICROCONTROLLERS, WHICH ARE WHAT MAKE OBJECTS INTERACTIVE

You are surrounded by dozens of them every day: they are embedded in timers, thermostats, toys, remote controls, microwave ovens, even some toothbrushes. They just do one specific task, and if you hardly notice them – which is often the case – it's because they are doing it well. They have been programmed to sense and control activity using sensors and actuators.

Sensors listen to the physical world. They convert energy that you give off when you press buttons, or wave your arms, or shout, into electrical signals. Buttons and knobs are sensors that you touch with your fingers, but there are many other kinds of sensors.

Actuators take action in the physical world. They convert electrical energy back into physical energy, like light and heat and movement.

Microcontrollers listen to sensors and talk to actuators. They decide what to do based on a program that you write.

Microcontrollers and the electronics you attach to them are just the skeleton of your projects, though. You'll need to bring skills you probably already have to put some flesh on the bones.

For example, in one of the projects we suggest, you'll make an arrow and attach it to a motor, and put them both in a box with a knob, so you can make a meter to tell people whether you're busy or not. In another, you'll put some lights and a tilt switch on a cardboard frame to make an hourglass.

Arduino can make your projects responsive, but only you can make them beautiful. We'll provide some suggestions along the way as to how you might do that.

Arduino was designed to help you get things done. To make that happen, we kept the background material on programming and electronics to a minimum. If you decide you want to know more about these aspects, there are lots of good guides available. We'll provide a couple of references, and you can find more online at: arduino.cc/starterkit

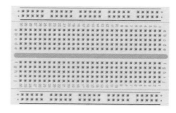

Arduino Uno - The microcontroller development board that will be at the heart of your projects. It's a simple computer, but one that has no way for you to interact with it yet. You will be building the circuits and interfaces for interaction, and telling the microcontroller how to interface with other components.

Battery Snap - Used to connect a 9V battery to power leads that can be easily plugged into a breadboard or your Arduino.

Breadboard - A board on which you can build electronic circuits. It's like a patch panel, with rows of holes that allow you to connect wires and components together. Versions that require soldering are available, as well as the solder-less type used here.

Capacitors - These components store and release electrical energy in a circuit. When the circuit's voltage is higher than what is stored in the capacitor, it allows current to flow in, giving the capacitor a charge. When the circuit's voltage is lower, the stored charge is released. Often placed across power and ground close to a sensor or motor to help smooth fluctuations in voltage.

DC motor - Converts electrical energy into mechanical energy when electricity is applied to its leads. Coils of wire inside the motor become magnetized when current flows through them.

These magnetic fields attract and repel magnets, causing the shaft to spin. If the direction of the electricity is reversed, the motor will spin in the opposite direction.

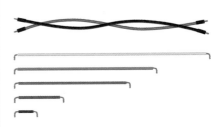

Diode - Ensures electricity flows only in one direction. Useful when you have a motor or other high current/voltage load in your circuit. Diodes are polarized, meaning that the direction that they're placed in a circuit matters. Placed one way, they allow current to pass through. Placed the other way, they block it. The anode side generally connects to the point of higher energy in your circuit. The cathode typically connects to the point of lower energy, or to ground. The cathode is usually marked with a band on one side of the component's body.

Jumper wires - Use these to connect components to each other on the breadboard, and to the Arduino.

Light Emitting Diodes (LEDs) - A type of diode that illuminates when electricity passes through it. Like all diodes, electricity only flows in one direction through these components. You're probably familiar with these as indicators on a variety of electronic devices. The anode, which typically connects to power, is usually the longer leg, and the cathode is the shorter leg.

Gels (red, green, blue) - These filter out different wavelengths of light. When used in conjunction with photoresistors, they cause the sensor to only react to the amount of light in the filtered color.

H-bridge - A circuit that allows you to control the polarity of the voltage applied to a load, usually a motor. The H-bridge in the kit is an integrated circuit, but it could also be constructed with a number of discrete components.

Liquid Crystal Display (LCD) - A type of alphanumeric or graphic display based on liquid crystals. LCDs are available in a many sizes, shapes, and styles. Yours has 2 rows with 16 characters each.

Male header pins - These pins fit into female sockets, like those on a breadboard. They help make connecting things much easier.

Potentiometer - A variable resistor with three pins. Two of the pins are connected to the ends of a fixed resistor. The middle pin, or wiper, moves across the resistor, dividing it into two halves. When the external sides of the potentiometer are connected to voltage and ground, the middle leg will give the difference in voltage as you turn the knob. Often referred to as a pot.

Optocoupler - This allows you to connect two circuits that do not share a common power supply. Internally there is a small LED that, when illuminated, causes a photoreceptor inside to close an internal switch. When you apply voltage to the + pin, the LED lights and the internal switch closes. The two outputs replace a switch in the second circuit.

Pushbuttons - Momentary switches that close a circuit when pressed. They snap into breadboards easily. These are good for detecting on/off signals.

Piezo - An electrical component that can be used to detect vibrations and create noises.

Phototransistor - Component that generates a current proportional to quantity of light absorbed.

Resistors - Resist the flow of electrical energy in a circuit, changing the voltage and current as a result. Resistor values are measured in ohms (represented by the Greek omega character: Ω). The colored stripes on the sides of resistors indicate their value (see resistor color code table, p. 41).

ling high current/high voltage components like motors. One pin connects to ground, another to the component being controlled, and the third connects to the Arduino. When the component receives voltage on the pin connected to an Arduino, it closes the circuit between the ground and the other component.

Servo motor - A type of geared motor that can only rotate 180 degrees. It is controlled by sending electrical pulses from your Arduino. These pulses tell the motor what position it should move to.

Temperature sensor - Changes its voltage output depending on the temperature of the component. The outside legs connect to power and ground. The voltage on the center pin changes as it gets warmer or cooler.

USB Cable - This allows you to connect your Arduino Uno to your personal computer for programming. It also provides power to the Arduino for most of the projects in the kit.

Tilt sensor - A type of switch that will open or close depending on its orientation. Typically they are hollow cylinders with a metal ball inside that will make a connection across two leads when tilted in the proper direction.

Transistor - A three legged device that can operate as an electronic switch. Useful for control-

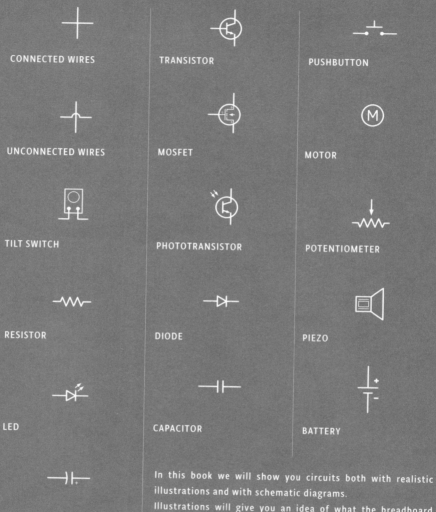

CONNECTED WIRES

UNCONNECTED WIRES

TILT SWITCH

RESISTOR

LED

POLARIZED CAPACITOR

GROUND

TRANSISTOR

MOSFET

PHOTOTRANSISTOR

DIODE

CAPACITOR

PUSHBUTTON

MOTOR

POTENTIOMETER

PIEZO

BATTERY

In this book we will show you circuits both with realistic illustrations and with schematic diagrams.

Illustrations will give you an idea of what the breadboard might look like in one possible implementation of the project. Schematics, instead, use symbols to capture the essence of circuits: they present the components and the ways they are connected in a clear, succinct, and unambiguous form, but not their physical organization. Schematics and schematic symbols are how we communicate about circuits. As you explore the world of electronics you will discover that some books and websites only provide schematic diagrams, so learning to read circuits this way is a valuable skill.

Here are the symbols we will be using throughout the book.

THE ARDUINO BOARD

Power connector

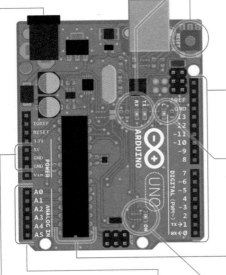

THE ARDUINO BOARD

Power connector
This is how you power your
Arduino when it's not plugged
into a USB port for power. Can
accept voltages between 7-12V.

USB port
Used for powering your
Arduino Uno, uploading your
sketches to your Arduino, and
for communicating with your
Arduino sketch (via `Serial.
println()` etc.)

Reset Button
Resets the ATmega
microcontroller.

TX and RX LEDs
These LEDs indicate communication between your Arduino
and your computer. Expect
them to flicker rapidly during
sketch upload as well as during
serial communication. Useful
for debugging.

Digital pins
Use these pins with
`digitalRead()`,
`digitalWrite()`,
and `analogWrite()`.
`analogWrite()` works only on
the pins with the PWM symbol.

Pin 13 LED
The only actuator built-in to
your Arduino Uno. Besides
being a handy target for your
first blink sketch, this LED is
very useful for debugging.

GND and 5V pins
Use these pins to provide +5V
power and ground to your
circuits.

Analog in
Use these pins with
`analogRead()`.

ATmega microcontroller
The heart of your Arduino Uno.

Power LED
Indicates that your Arduino
is receiving power. Useful for
debugging.

Your Starter Kit includes a pre-cut, easy-to-assemble wooden base that will make working on all your projects – whether they are from this book or not – even easier.

To build it, take the wood sheet out of the box and follow the instructions on the right.

Be careful to use only the parts that are shown, but don't misplace any of the other pieces: you'll need them for some of the projects later.

Let's start!

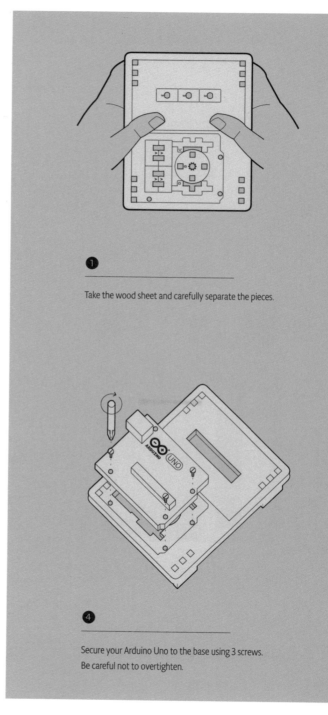

1

Take the wood sheet and carefully separate the pieces.

4

Secure your Arduino Uno to the base using 3 screws. Be careful not to overtighten.

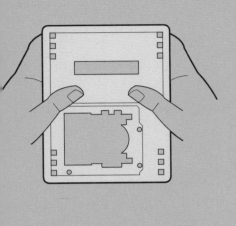

2

Go on until you've separated all the parts.

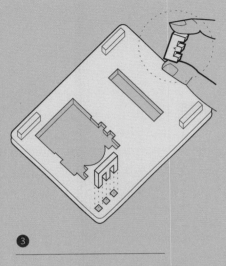

3

Place the pieces marked with an "A" into the holes in the corners, in order to create the feet of the base.

5

Carefully peel the backing from the breadboard.

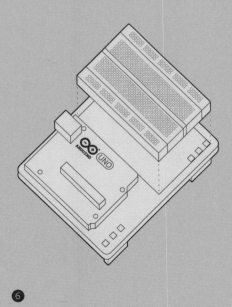

6

Stick the breadboard on the wooden sheet, next to the Arduino Uno.

THINGS YOU NEED TO SUPPLY

9V battery

Small light source like a flashlight

Conductive material like
aluminum foil or copper mesh

Colored paper

Scissors

An old CD or DVD

Tape and glue

A box that you can make
holes into

Basic tools like a screwdriver

9V battery powered component
Any battery powered electronic device with
at least one switch or pushbutton that you're
willing to hack into will do the job.

Soldering iron and solder
(necessary only in Project 15)

SETTING UP

BEFORE YOU START CONTROLLING THE WORLD AROUND
YOU, YOU'LL NEED TO DOWNLOAD THE IDE TO PROGRAM
YOUR BOARD

The Arduino IDE allows you to write programs and upload them
to your Arduino.

Download the latest version of the IDE from:
`arduino.cc/download`

**Have your Arduino board and USB cable near your computer.
Don't plug them in just yet.**

Follow the appropriate procedures in the next pages for
Windows, Mac OS X or Linux.

The online version of this guide is available at:
`arduino.cc/guide`

WINDOWS
INSTALLATION

Online version

arduino.cc/windows

WINDOWS 7, VISTA,
AND XP

1 After finishing the download, double-click on the file "Install Arduino". If a security warning window shows up, click on "Run" or "Allow" and accept the License Agreement. Click on "Next" to choose the folder to install the IDE and then click on "Install".

2 Connect the Arduino to the computer with the USB cable. The board will automatically draw power from the USB connection of the computer and the green LED (labeled ON) will turn on.

3 Windows should initiate its driver installation process when the board is plugged in. Your computer won't be able to find the drivers by itself; you need to point it to the proper folder.
— Windows XP: If Windows Update asks about the path for the software, select "Yes, for this time only" and then "Install from a list or specific location";
— Vista or Windows 7: On Windows 7, if a popup window asks you to install the driver automatically or to look for it in the computer, choose to look for the driver on your computer. On Vista, continue directly to the next step by selecting the recommended choice.

4 If the installation doesn't start automatically, click on the Start Menu and open the Control Panel. Then, go to the device manager following these paths:
— Windows XP: Switch to Classic View -> System -> Hardware -> Device Manager
— Windows Vista: Classic View -> Device Manager
— Windows 7: System and Security -> System -> Device Manager

5 Look for the Arduino device under the category "Other devices" or "Unknown Devices" and select "Update Driver" or "Update Driver Software" clicking with the right button of the mouse.

6 Click on "Browse" and select the "Drivers" folder (not the folder "FTDI USB Drivers") in the Arduino folder. Press "OK" and "Next". If a dialog box about a test on the Windows Logo shows up, click on "Continue Anyway". Windows will now install the driver.

7 In the "Device Manager", under "Ports (COM & LPT)", you should see a port similar to "Arduino UNO (COM4)".

Congratulations! You've installed the Arduino IDE on the computer.

MAC OS X
INSTALLATION

Online version
arduino.cc/mac

OS X 10.5 AND LATER

1 If you are using 10.8 (Mountain Lion) or later, go to System Preferences and open the "Security & Privacy" panel. In the "General" tab, under the heading "Allow applications downloded from", click the toggle for "Anywhere".

2 Once the Arduino IDE has finished downloading, double-click on the .zip file to expand the application.

3 Copy the Arduino application to the Applications folder, or anywhere else you wish to install the software.

4 Connect your Arduino to the computer with the USB cable. The board will be automatically powered from the USB connection and the green LED (labeled ON) will turn on.

5 You do not need to install any drivers to work with the board.

6 Depending on the version of OS X that you are running, you might get a dialog box asking if you wish to open the "System Preferences". Click the "Network Preferences" button and click "Apply".

7 The Uno will show up as "Not Configured", but it is already working. You can quit System Preferences.

Congratulations! You have Arduino all set up and you're ready to start making projects.

LINUX
INSTALLATION

If you're using Linux, please visit the website for instructions.
arduino.cc/linux

COMMUNICATING WITH THE ARDUINO

Now that you've installed the Arduino IDE and made sure your computer can talk to the board, it's time to make sure you can up-load a program.

1 Double-click the Arduino application to open it. If the IDE loads in the wrong language, you can change this in the application preferences. Look for "Language Support" on this page for de-tails: *arduino.cc/ide*

2 Navigate to the LED Blink example sketch ('sketch' is what Ar-duino programs are called). It's located under:

FILE > EXAMPLES > 01.BASICS > BLINK

3 A window with some text in it should have opened. Leave the window be for now, and select your board under:

TOOLS > BOARD

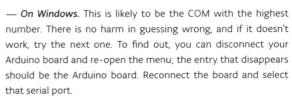

4 Choose the serial port your Arduino is connected to from the *TOOLS > SERIAL PORT* menu.

— *On Windows.* This is likely to be the COM with the highest number. There is no harm in guessing wrong, and if it doesn't work, try the next one. To find out, you can disconnect your Arduino board and re-open the menu; the entry that disappears should be the Arduino board. Reconnect the board and select that serial port.

— *On Mac.* This should be something with /dev/tty.usbmodem in it. There are usually two of these; select either one.

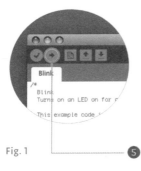

Fig. 1

5 To upload the Blink sketch to your Arduino, press the **UPLOAD** toggle in the top left corner of the window. See Fig. 1.

6 You should see a bar indicating the progress of the upload near the lower left corner of the Arduino IDE, and the lights labeled TX and RX on the Arduino board will be blinking. If the upload is successful, the IDE will display the message **DONE UPLOADING**.

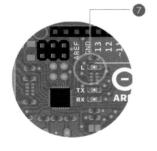

7 A few seconds after the upload has completed, you should see the yellow LED with an *L* next to it start blinking. See Fig. 2.
If this is the case, congratulations! You've successfully programmed the Arduino to blink its onboard LED!

Sometimes your brand new Arduino is already programmed with the Blink sketch, so you can't tell if you are truly in control. If this is the case, change the `delay` time by changing the number in the parenthesis to 100, and upload the Blink sketch again. Now the LED should blink much faster.
Congratulations! You really are in control! Now it's time to move on to Project 1. (You needn't save any changes you have made.)

Fig. 2

ADDITIONAL INFORMATION

If you have problems with any of the steps outlined above, please see the troubleshooting suggestions:
arduino.cc/trouble

While you're getting ready to build your projects, you can look at the following page for additional information about the Arduino's programming environment:
arduino.cc/ide

You might also want to look at:

— the examples for using various sensors and actuators
arduino.cc/tutorial

— the reference for the Arduino language
arduino.cc/examples

Ø1

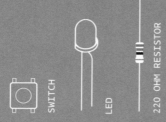

SWITCH

LED

220 OHM RESISTOR

INGREDIENTS

GET TO KNOW YOUR TOOLS

YOU'LL MAKE A SIMPLE CIRCUIT WITH SOME
SWITCHES, AN LED, AND A RESISTOR

*Discover: basic electrical theory, how a breadboard works,
components in series and parallel*

Time: **30 MINUTES**

Level: ■ ■ ■ ■ ■

*Electricity is a type of energy, much like heat, gravity, or light. Electrical energy
flows through conductors, like wire. You can convert electrical energy into other
forms of energy to do something interesting, like turn on a light or make some
noise out of a speaker.*

The components you might use to do this, like speakers or light bulbs, are electrical **transducers**. Transducers change other types of energy into electrical energy and vice versa. Things that convert other forms of energy into electrical energy are often called **sensors**, and things that convert electrical energy into other forms of energy are sometimes called **actuators**. You will be building **circuits** to move electricity through different components. Circuits are closed loops of wire with a power source (like a battery) and something to do something useful with the energy, called a load.

In a circuit, electricity flows from a point of higher potential energy (usually referred to as power or +) to a point of lower potential energy. Ground (often represented with a - or GND) is generally the point of least potential energy in a circuit. In the circuits you are building, electricity only flows in one direction. This type of circuit is called direct current, or DC. In alternating current (AC) circuits electricity changes its direction 50 or 60 times a second (depending on where you live). This is the type of electricity that comes from a wall socket.

There are a few terms you should be familiar with when working with electrical circuits. **Current** (measured in amperes, or amps; with the **A** symbol) is the amount of electrical charge flowing past a specific point in your circuit. **Voltage** (measured in volts; with the **V** symbol) is the difference in energy between one point in a circuit and another. And finally, **resistance** (measured in ohms; with the Ω symbol) is how much a component resists the flow of electrical energy.

One way to imagine this is to think about a rockslide going down a cliff, as shown in Fig. 1. The higher the cliff, the more energy the rocks will have when they hit the bottom. The height of the cliff is like the voltage in a circuit: the higher the voltage at the energy source, the more energy you have to use. The more rocks you have, the more energy is being carried down the cliff. The number of rocks is like the current in an electrical circuit. The rocks go through bushes on the side of the cliff, losing some energy in the process; the energy is used up to crush the bushes. The bushes are like resistors in a circuit, offering resistance to the electrical flow and converting it into other forms of energy.

Rockslide as a metaphor for electrical current flow.
Fig. 1

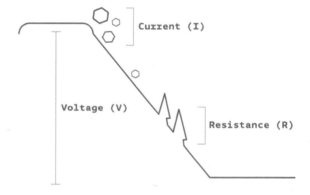

A COUPLE OF THINGS ABOUT CIRCUITS

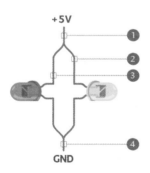

The current at (1) = current at (2) + current at (3) = current at (4).
Fig. 2

— There needs to be a complete path from the energy source (power) to the point of least energy (ground) to make a circuit. If there's no path for the energy to travel, the circuit won't work.

— All the electrical energy gets used up in a circuit by the components in it. Each component converts some of the energy into another form of energy. In any circuit, all of the voltage is converted to another form of energy (light, heat, sound, etc.).

— The flow of current at a specific point in a circuit will always be the same coming in and going out.

— Electrical current will seek the path of least resistance to ground. Given two possible paths, more of the electrical current will go down the path with less resistance. If you have a connection that connects power and ground together with no resistance, you will cause a short circuit, and the current will try to follow that path. In a short circuit, the power source and wires convert the electrical energy into light and heat, usually as sparks or an explosion. If you've ever shorted out a battery and seen sparks, you know how dangerous a short circuit can be.

WHAT'S A BREADBOARD?

The breadboard is the primary place you will be building circuits. The one that comes in your kit is solderless, so named because you don't have to solder anything together, sort of like LEGO in electronic form. The horizontal and vertical rows of the breadboard, as shown in Fig. 3, carry electrictricity through thin metal connectors under the plastic with holes.

The 5 holes in each horizontal row are connected electrically through metal strips inside the breadboard.

The middle row breaks the connection between the two sides of the board.

The vertical strips that run the length of the breadboard are electrically connected. The strips are usually used for power and ground connections.

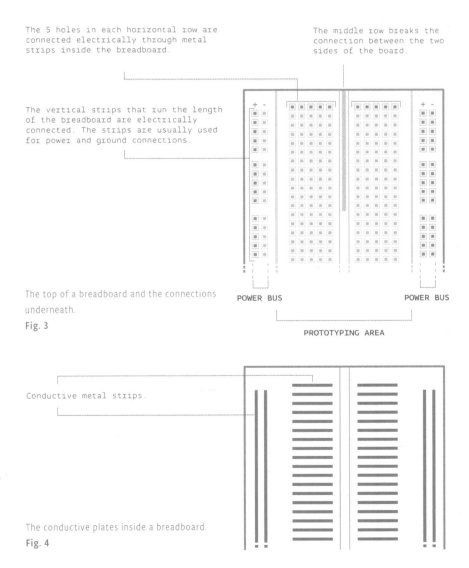

The top of a breadboard and the connections underneath.

Fig. 3

POWER BUS

POWER BUS

PROTOTYPING AREA

Conductive metal strips.

The conductive plates inside a breadboard.

Fig. 4

CIRCUIT DRAWINGS

Throughout these projects, you'll see two views of circuits: one in breadboard view (like in Fig. 5), that looks like the stuff in your kit. The other is a schematic view (like in Fig. 6), which is a more abstract way of showing the relationships between components in a circuit. Schematics don't always show where components are placed relative to each other, but they show how they are connected.

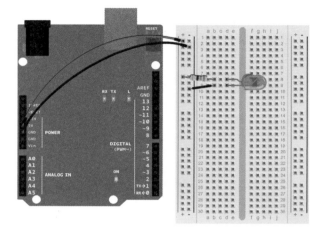

Circuit illustration.

Fig. 5

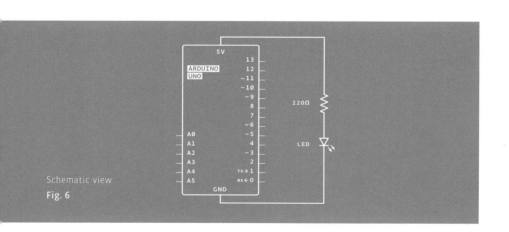

Schematic view

Fig. 6

YOUR FIRST COMPONENTS

CATHODE

ANODE

An *LED*, or light-emitting diode, is a component that converts electrical energy into light energy. LEDs are polarized components, which means they only allow electricity to flow through them in one direction. The longer leg on the LED is called an anode, it will connect to power. The shorter leg is a cathode and will connect to ground. When voltage is applied to the anode of the LED, and the cathode is connected to ground, the LED emits light.

A *resistor* is a component that resists the flow of electrical energy (see the components list for an explanation on the colored stripes on the side). It converts some of the electrical energy into heat. If you put a resistor in series with a component like an LED, the resistor will use up some of the electrical energy and the LED will receive less energy as a result. This allows you to supply components with the amount of energy they need. You use a resistor in series with the LED to keep it from receiving too much voltage. Without the resistor, the LED would be brighter for a few moments, but quickly burn out.

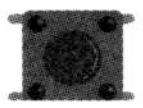

A *switch* interrupts the flow of electricity, breaking the circuit when open. When a switch is closed, it will complete a circuit. There are many types of switches. The ones in your kit are called momentary switches, or pushbuttons, because they are only closed when pressure is applied.

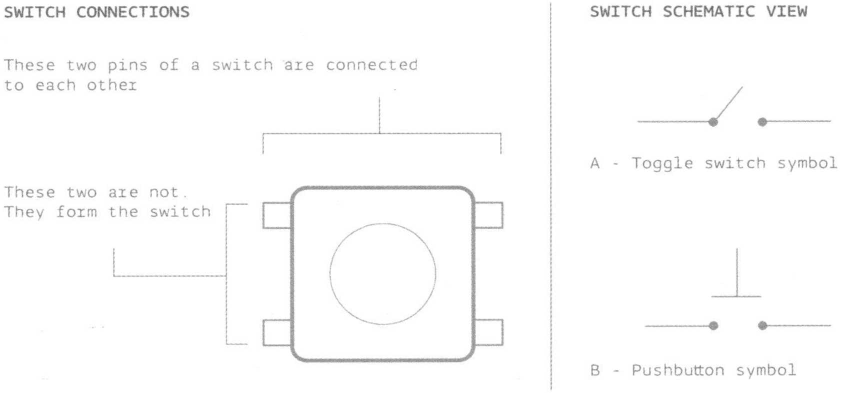

SWITCH CONNECTIONS

These two pins of a switch are connected to each other

These two are not. They form the switch

SWITCH SCHEMATIC VIEW

A - Toggle switch symbol

B - Pushbutton symbol

The switch
Fig. 7

BUILD THE
CIRCUIT

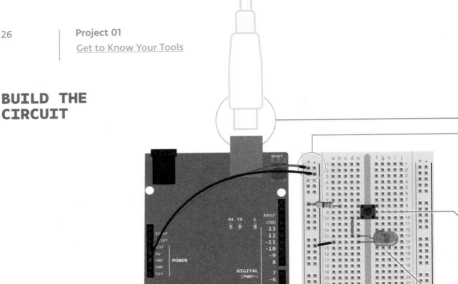

Fig. 8

Your first interactive circuit, using a switch, a resistor and an LED. Arduino is just the power source for this circuit; in later projects, you'll connect its input and output pins to control more complex circuits.

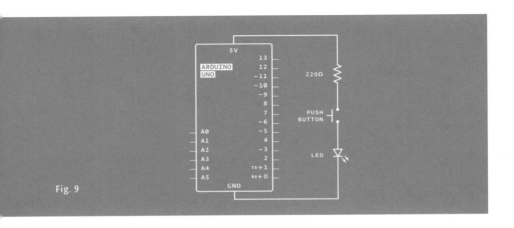

Fig. 9

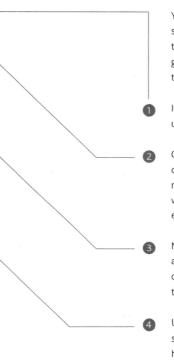

You're going to use the Arduino in this project, but only as a source of power. When plugged into a USB port or a 9-volt battery, the Arduino will provide 5 volts between its 5V pin and its ground pin that you can use. 5V = 5 volts, you'll see it written this way a lot.

1 If your Arduino is connected to a battery or computer via USB, unplug it before building the circuit!

2 Connect a red wire to the 5V pin on the Arduino, and put the other end in one of the long bus lines in your breadboard. Connect ground on the Arduino to the adjacent bus line with a black wire. It's helpful to keep your wire color consistent (red for power, black for ground) throughout your circuit.

3 Now that you have power on your board, place your switch across the center of the board. The switch will sit across the center in one direction. The bend in the legs of the switch points to the center of the board.

4 Use a 220-ohm resistor to connect power to one side of the switch. The illustrations in this book use 4 bands. Your kit may have a mix of 4 and 5 band resistors. Use the illustration on the side to check for the right one for this project. Look at page 41 for a detailed explanation of the color codes for resistors.
On the other side of the switch, connect the anode (long leg) of the LED. With a wire connect the cathode (short leg) of the LED to ground. When you're ready, plug the USB cable into the Arduino.

USE IT

Once everything is set to go, press the button. You should see the LED light up. Congratulations, you just made a circuit! Once you've tired of pressing the button to turn the light on, it's time to shake things up by adding a second button.

You'll be placing components on the breadboard in series and in parallel. Components in series come one after another. Components in parallel run side by side.

Series circuit
COMPONENTS IN SERIES COME ONE AFTER ANOTHER

Once you've removed your power source add a switch next to the one already on your breadboard. Wire them together in series as shown in Fig. 10. Connect the anode (long leg) up the LED to the second switch. Connect the LED cathode to ground. Power up the Arduino again: now to turn on the LED, you need to press both switches. Since these are in series, they both need to be closed for the circuit to be completed.

These two elements are in series

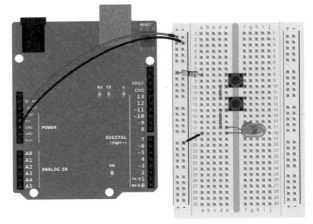

The two switches are in series. This means that the same electrical current flows through both of them, so that they both have to be pressed for the LED to light up.
Fig. 10

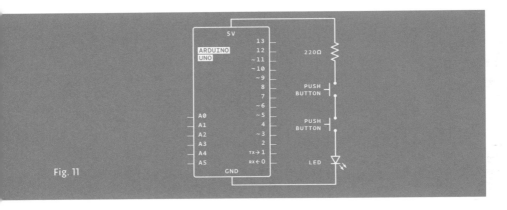
Fig. 11

These two elements
are in parallel

Parallel circuit
COMPONENTS IN PARALLEL RUN SIDE BY SIDE

Now that you've mastered the art of things in series, it's time to wire up switches in parallel. Keep the switches and LED where they are, but remove the connection between the two switches. Wire both switches to the resistor. Attach the other end of both switches to the LED, as shown in Fig. 12. Now when you press either button, the circuit is completed and the light turns on.

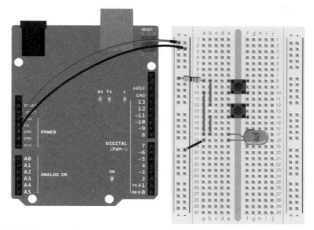

These two switches are in parallel. This means that the electrical current is split between them. If either switch is pressed, the LED will light up.
Fig. 12

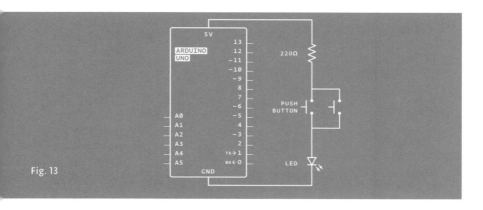

Fig. 13

UNDERSTANDING OHM'S LAW

$$V = I * R \qquad I = V / R \qquad R = V / I$$

You can use this circle to remember the relationships between voltage, current, and resistance. Put your finger over any of the three, and you see how it relates to the other two.

Current, voltage, and resistance are all related. When you change one of these in a circuit, it affects the others. The relationship between them is known as Ohm's Law, named for Georg Simon Ohm, who discovered it.

VOLTAGE (V) = CURRENT (I) * RESISTANCE (R)

When measuring amperage in the circuits you'll be building, values will be in the milliamp range. That's thousandths of one amp.

In the circuit shown in Fig. 5, you're supplying 5 volts. The resistor offers 220 ohms resistance. To find the amperage used by the LED, replace the values in the equation. You should have 5=I*220. Dividing both sides of the equation by 220, you'll find that I = .023. That's 23 thousandths of an amp, or 23 milliamps (23 mA) used by the LED. That value is just about the maximum you can safely use with these LEDs, which is why you used a 220-ohm resistor.

You can expand this project in a number of ways, either by creating your own switch (two pieces of foil with wire work well), or creating a combination of switches and LEDs in parallel and series. What happens when you put three or four LEDs in series? What happens when they are in parallel? Why does it behave the way it does?

A *multimeter* is a tool that can verify the amount of resistance, current, and voltage in your circuit. While it's not necessary to use one for these projects, it can be a useful part of any engineer's toolbox. There's a good description of how to use one online at *arduino.cc/multimeter*

You've learned about the electrical properties of voltage, current, and resistance while building a circuit on a breadboard. With some components like LEDs, resistors and switches, you created the simplest interactive system: a user presses the button, the lights turn on. These fundamentals of working with electronics will be referenced and expanded upon in the upcoming projects.

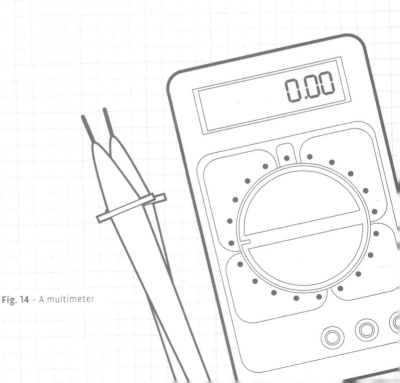

Fig. 14 - A multimeter

02

SWITCH

LED

220 OHM RESISTOR

10 KILOHM RESISTOR

INGREDIENTS

SPACESHIP INTERFACE

YOUR ARDUINO IS GOING TO STAR IN A SCIENCE
FICTION MOVIE

| Discover: digital input and output, your first program, variables

Time: **45 MINUTES** | Builds on project: **1**
Level: ■ ■ ■ ■ ■

Now that you've got the basics of electricity under control, it's time to move onto
controlling things with your Arduino. In this project, you'll be building something
that could have been a spaceship interface in a 1970s science fiction movie. You'll
make a cool control panel with a switch and lights that turn on when you press the
switch. You can decide whether the lights mean "Engage Hyperdrive" or "Fire the
lasers!". A green LED will be on, until you press a button. When the Arduino gets
a signal from the button, the green light will turn off and 2 other lights will start
blinking.

The Arduino's digital pins can read only two states: when there is voltage on an
input pin, and when there's not. This kind of input is normally called digital (or
sometimes binary, for two-states). These states are commonly referred to as
HIGH and **LOW**. **HIGH** is the same as saying "there's voltage here!" and **LOW** means
"there's no voltage on this pin!". When you turn an **OUTPUT** pin **HIGH** using a
command called `digitalWrite()`, you're turning it on. Measure the voltage
between the pin and ground, you'll get 5 volts. When you turn an **OUTPUT** pin
LOW, you're turning it off.

The Arduino's digital pins can act as both inputs and outputs. In your code, you'll
configure them depending on what you want their function to be. When the pins
are outputs, you can turn on components like LEDs. If you configure the pins as
inputs, you can check if a switch is being pressed or not. Since pins 0 and 1 are used
for communicating with the computer, it's best to start with pin 2.

BUILD THE
CIRCUIT

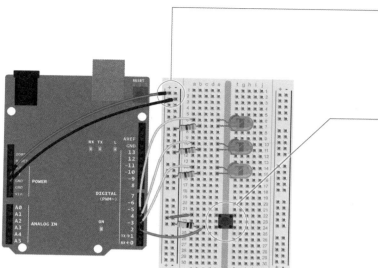

Fig. 1

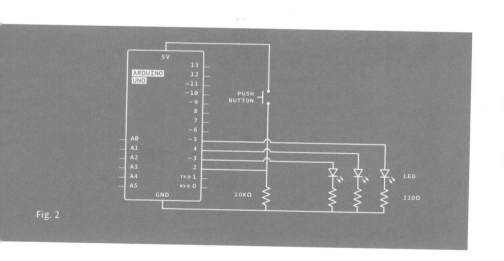

Fig. 2

1. Wire up your breadboard to the Arduino's 5V and ground connections, just like the previous project. Place the two red LEDs and one green LED on the breadboard. Attach the cathode (short leg) of each LED to ground through a 220-ohm resistor. Connect the anode (long leg) of the green LED to pin 3. Connect the red LEDs' anodes to pins 4 and 5, respectively.

2. Place the switch on the breadboard just as you did in the previous project. Attach one side to power, and the other side to digital pin 2 on the Arduino. You'll also need to add a 10k-ohm resistor from ground to the switch pin that connects to the Arduino. That pull-down resistor connects the pin to ground when the switch is open, so it reads **LOW** when there is no voltage coming in through the switch.

You can cover the breadboard with the template provided in the kit. Or you can decorate it to make your own launch system. The lights turning on and off mean nothing by themselves, but when you put them in a control panel and give them labels, they gain meaning. What do you want the green LED to mean? What do the flashing red LEDs mean? You decide!

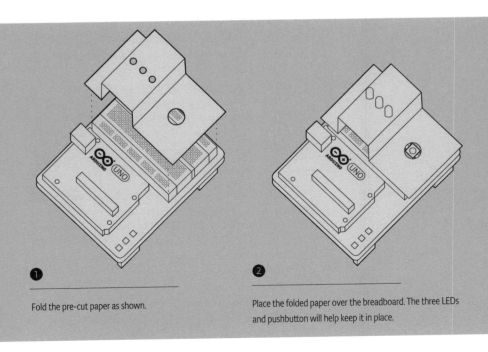

1 Fold the pre-cut paper as shown.

2 Place the folded paper over the breadboard. The three LEDs and pushbutton will help keep it in place.

THE CODE

Some notes before you start

Every Arduino program has two main functions. Functions are parts of a computer program that run specific commands. Functions have unique names, and are "called" when needed. The necessary functions in an Arduino program are called setup( ) and loop( ). These functions need to be declared, which means that you need to tell the Arduino what these functions will do. setup( ) and loop( ) are declared as you see on the right.

In this program, you're going to create a variable before you get into the main part of the program. Variables are names you give to places in the Arduino's memory so you can keep track of what is happening. These values can change depending on your program's instructions.

Variable names should be descriptive of whatever value they are storing. For example, a variable named switchState tells you what it stores: the state of a switch. On the other hand, a variable named "x" doesn't tell you much about what it stores.

Let's start coding

To create a variable, you need to declare what *type* it is. The *data type* int will hold a whole number (also called an *integer*); that's any number without a decimal point. When you declare a variable, you usually give it an initial value as well. The declaration of the variable as every statement must end with a semicolon (;).

Configure pin functionality

The setup( ) runs once, when the Arduino is first powered on. This is where you configure the digital pins to be either inputs or outputs using a function named pinMode( ). The pins connected to LEDs will be OUTPUTs and the switch pin will be an INPUT.

Create the loop function

The loop( ) runs continuously after the setup( ) has completed. The loop( ) is where you'll check for voltage on the inputs, and turn outputs on and off. To check the voltage level on a digital input, you use the function digitalRead( ) that checks the chosen pin for voltage. To know what pin to check, digitalRead( ) expects an *argument*.

Arguments are information that you pass to functions, telling them how they should do their job. For example, digitalRead( ) needs one argument: what pin to check. In your program, digitalRead( ) is going to check the state of

```
void setup(){
}

void loop(){
}
```

{ Curly brackets }
Any code you write inside the curly brackets will be executed when the function is called.

```
1 int switchState = 0;
```

```
2 void setup(){
3   pinMode(3,OUTPUT);
4   pinMode(4,OUTPUT);
5   pinMode(5,OUTPUT);
6   pinMode(2,INPUT);
7 }
```

Case sensitivity
Pay attention to the case sensitivity in your code. For example, pinMode is the name of a command, but pinmode will produce an error.

```
8 void loop(){
9   switchState = digitalRead(2);
10  // this is a comment
```

Comments
If you ever want to include natural language in your program, you can leave a comment.
Comments are notes you leave for yourself that the computer ignores. To write a comment, add two slashes //
The computer will ignore anything on the line after those slashes.

pin 2 and store the value in the switchState variable. If there's voltage on the pin when digitalRead( ) is called, the switchState variable will get the value HIGH (or 1). If there is no voltage on the pin, switchState will get the value LOW (or 0).

The if statement

Above, you used the word if to check the state of something (namely, the switch position). An if( ) statement in programming compares two things, and determines whether the comparison is true or false. Then it performs actions you tell it to do. When comparing two things in programming, you use two equal signs ==. If you use only one sign, you will be setting a value instead of comparing it.

Build up your spaceship

digitalWrite( ) is the command that allows you to send 5V or 0V to an output pin. digitalWrite( ) takes two arguments: what pin to control, and what value to set that pin HIGH or LOW. If you want to turn the red LEDs on and the green LED off inside your if( ) statement, your code would look like this .

If you run your program now, the lights will change when you press the switch. That's pretty neat, but you can add a little more complexity to the program for a more interesting output.

You've told the Arduino what to do when the switch is open. Now define what happens when the switch is closed. The if( ) statement has an optional else component that allows for something to happen if the original condition is not met. In this case, since you checked to see if the switch was LOW, write code for the HIGH condition after the else statement.

To get the red LEDs to blink when the button is pressed, you'll need to turn the lights off and on in the else statement you just wrote. To do this, change the code to look like this.

Now your program will flash the red LEDs when the switch button is pressed.

After setting the LEDs to a certain state, you'll want the Arduino to pause for a moment before changing them back. If you don't wait, the lights will go back and forth so fast that it will appear as if they are just a little dim, not on and off. This is because the Arduino goes through its loop( ) thousands of times each second, and the LED will be turned on and off quicker than we can perceive. The delay( ) function lets you stop the Arduino from executing anything for a period of time. delay( ) takes an argument that determines the number of milliseconds before it executes the next set of code. There are 1000 milliseconds in one second. delay(250) will pause for a quarter second.

It can be helpful to write out the flow of your program in pseudocode: a way of describing what you want the program to do in plain language, but structured in a way that makes it easy to write a real program from it. In this case you're going to determine if `switchState` is HIGH (meaning the button is pressed) or not. If the switch is pressed, you'll turn the green LED off and the red ones on. In pseudocode, the statement could look like this:

```
11    if (switchState == LOW) {
12    // the button is not pressed
```

```
if the switchState is LOW:
    turn the green LED on
    turn the red LEDs off

if the switchState is HIGH:
    turn the green LED off
    turn the red LEDs on
```

```
13        digitalWrite(3, HIGH); // green LED
14        digitalWrite(4, LOW);  // red LED
15        digitalWrite(5, LOW);  // red LED
16    }
```

```
17    else {  // the button is pressed
18        digitalWrite(3, LOW);
19        digitalWrite(4, LOW);
20        digitalWrite(5, HIGH);
```

```
21        delay(250);  // wait for a quarter second
22        // toggle the LEDs
23        digitalWrite(4, HIGH);
24        digitalWrite(5, LOW);
25        delay(250); // wait for a quarter second
```

```
26    }
27 } // go back to the beginning of the loop
```

USE IT

Once your Arduino is programmed, you should see the green light turn on. When you press the switch, the red lights will start flashing, and the green light will turn off. Try changing the time of the two `delay()` functions; notice what happens to the lights and how the response of the system changes depending on the speed of the flashing. When you call a `delay()` in your program, it stops all other functionality. No sensor readings will happen until that time period has passed. While delays are often useful, when designing your own projects make sure they are not unnecessarily interfering with your interface.

How would you get the red LEDs to be blinking when your program starts? How could you make a larger, or more complex interface for your interstellar adventures with LEDs and switches?

When you start creating an interface for your project, think about what people's expectations are while using it. When they press a button, will they want immediate feedback? Should there be a delay between their action and what the Arduino does? Try and place yourself in the shoes of a different user while you design, and see if your expectations match up to the reality of your project.

In this project, you created your first Arduino program to control the behavior of some LEDs based on a switch. You've used variables, an if()...else statement, and functions to read the state of an input and control outputs.

HOW TO READ RESISTOR COLOR CODES

Resistor values are marked using colored bands, according to a code developed in the 1920s, when it was too difficult to write numbers on such tiny objects.

Each color corresponds to a number, like you see in the table below. Each resistor has either 4 or 5 bands. In the 4-band type, the first two bands indicate the first two digits of the value while the third one indicates the number of zeroes that follow (technically it reprents the power of ten). The last band specifies the tolerance: in the example below, gold indicates that the resistor value can be 10k ohm plus or minus 5%.

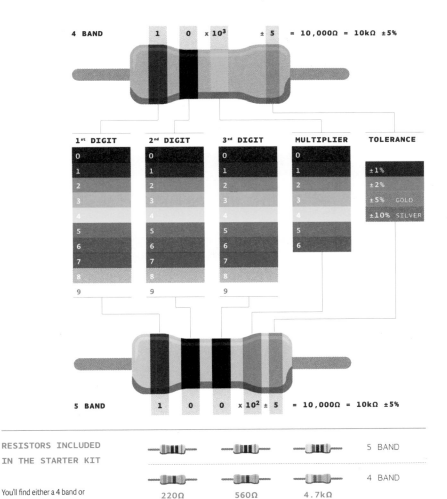

4 BAND   1   0   x 10^3 ± 5   = 10,000Ω = 10kΩ ±5%

1ˢᵗ DIGIT	2ⁿᵈ DIGIT	3ʳᵈ DIGIT	MULTIPLIER	TOLERANCE
0	0	0	0	
1	1	1	1	±1%
2	2	2	2	±2%
3	3	3	3	±5% GOLD
4	4	4	4	±10% SILVER
5	5	5	5	
6	6	6	6	
7	7	7		
8	8	8		
9	9	9		

5 BAND   1   0   0   x 10^2 ± 5   = 10,000Ω = 10kΩ ±5%

RESISTORS INCLUDED IN THE STARTER KIT

You'll find either a 4 band or a 5 band version.

5 BAND
4 BAND

220Ω   560Ω   4.7kΩ

5 BAND
4 BAND

1kΩ   10kΩ   1MΩ   10MΩ

03

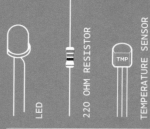

LED   220 OHM RESISTOR   TEMPERATURE SENSOR

INGREDIENTS

LOVE-O-METER

TURN THE ARDUINO INTO A LOVE MACHINE. USING AN
ANALOG INPUT, YOU'RE GOING TO REGISTER JUST HOW
HOT YOU REALLY ARE!

Discover: analog Input, using the serial monitor

Time: **45 MINUTES**
Level: ■ ■ ■ ■ ■

Builds on projects: **1, 2**

While switches and buttons are great, there's a lot more to the physical world than on and off. Even though the Arduino is a digital tool, it's possible for it to get information from analog sensors to measure things like temperature or light. To do this, you'll take advantage of the Arduino's built-in Analog-to-Digital Converter (ADC). Analog in pins A0-A5 can report back a value between 0-1023, which maps to a range from 0 volts to 5 volts.

You'll be using a *temperature sensor* to measure how warm your skin is. This component outputs a changing voltage depending on the temperature it senses. It has three pins: one that connects to ground, another that connects to power, and a third that outputs a variable voltage to your Arduino. In the sketch for this project, you'll read the sensor's output and use it to turn LEDs on and off, indicating how warm you are. There are several different models of temperature sensor. This model, the TMP36, is convenient because it outputs a voltage that changes directly proportional to the temperature in degrees Celsius.

The Arduino IDE comes with a tool called the *serial monitor* that enables you to report back results from the microcontroller. Using the serial monitor, you can get information about the status of sensors, and get an idea about what is happening in your circuit and code as it runs.

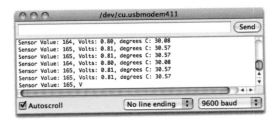

Serial monitor

Fig. 1

BUILD THE
CIRCUIT

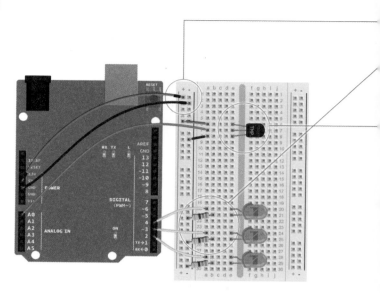

Fig. 2

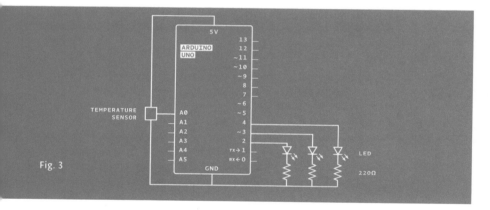

Fig. 3

In this project, you need to check the ambient temperature of the room before proceeding. You're checking things manually right now, but this can also be accomplished through calibration. It's possible to use a button to set the baseline temperature, or to have the Arduino take a sample before starting the `loop( )` and use that as the reference point. Project 6 gets into details about this, or you can look at the Calibration example that comes bundled with the Arduino software:
arduino.cc/en/calibration

1. Just as you've been doing in the earlier projects, wire up your breadboard so you have power and ground.

2. Attach the cathode (short leg) of each of the LEDs you're using to ground through a 220-ohm resistor. Connect the anodes of the LEDs to pins 2 through 4. These will be the indicators for the project.

3. Place the TMP36 on the breadboard with the rounded part facing away from the Arduino (the order of the pins is important!) as shown in Fig. 2. Connect the left pin of the flat facing side to power, and the right pin to ground. Connect the center pin to pin A0 on your Arduino. This is analog input pin 0.

Create an interface for your sensor for people interact with. A paper cutout in the shape of a hand is a good indicator. If you're feeling lucky, create a set of lips for someone to kiss, see how well that lights things up! You might also want to label the LEDs to give them some meaning. Maybe one LED means you're a cold fish, two LEDs means you're warm and friendly, and three LEDs means you're too hot to handle!

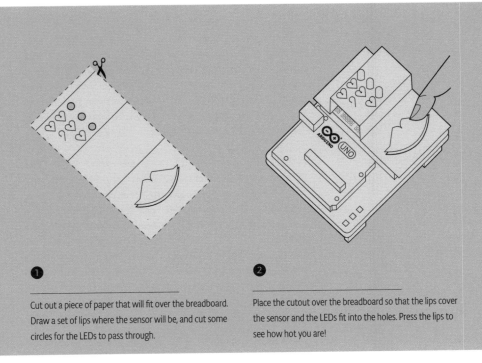

1 Cut out a piece of paper that will fit over the breadboard. Draw a set of lips where the sensor will be, and cut some circles for the LEDs to pass through.

2 Place the cutout over the breadboard so that the lips cover the sensor and the LEDs fit into the holes. Press the lips to see how hot you are!

THE CODE

A pair of useful constants

Constants are similar to variables in that they allow you to uniquely name things in the program, but unlike variables they cannot change. Name the analog input for easy reference, and create another named constant to hold the baseline temperature. For every 2 degrees above this baseline, an LED will turn on. You've already seen the int datatype, used here to identify which pin the sensor is on. The temperature is being stored as a *float*, or floating-point number. This type of number has a decimal point, and is used for numbers that can be expressed as fractions.

Initialize the serial port to the desired speed

In the setup you're going to use a new command, **Serial. begin()**. This opens up a connection between the Arduino and the computer, so you can see the values from the analog input on your computer screen.
The argument **9600** is the speed at which the Arduino will communicate, 9600 bits per second. You will use the Arduino IDE's serial monitor to view the information you choose to send from your microcontroller. When you open the IDE's serial monitor verify that the baud rate is 9600.

Initialize the digital pin directions and turn off

Next up is a **for()** loop to set some pins as outputs. These are the pins that you attached LEDs to earlier. Instead of giving them unique names and typing out the **pinMode()** function for each one, you can use a **for()** loop to go through them all quickly. This is a handy trick if you have a large number of similar things you wish to iterate through in a program. Tell the **for()** loop to run through pins 2 to 4 sequentially.

Read the temperature sensor

In the **loop()**, you'll use a local variable named **sensorVal** to store the reading from your sensor. To get the value from the sensor, you call **analogRead()** that takes one argument: what pin it should take a voltage reading on. The value, which is between 0 and 1023, is a representation of the voltage on the pin.

Send the temperature sensor values to the computer

The function **Serial.print()** sends information from the Arduino to a connected computer. You can see this information in your serial monitor. If you give **Serial.print()** an argument in quotation marks, it will print out the text you typed. If you give it a variable as an argument, it will print out the value of that variable.

```
1 const int sensorPin = A0;
2 const float baselineTemp = 20.0;
```

```
3 void setup(){
4   Serial.begin(9600); // open a serial port
```

```
5   for(int pinNumber = 2; pinNumber<5; pinNumber++){
6     pinMode(pinNumber,OUTPUT);
7     digitalWrite(pinNumber, LOW);
8   }
9 }
```

for() loop tutorial
arduino.cc/for

```
10 void loop(){
11   int sensorVal = analogRead(sensorPin);
```

```
12   Serial.print("Sensor Value: ");
13   Serial.print(sensorVal);
```

Convert sensor reading to voltage

With a little math, it's possible to figure out what the real voltage on the pin is. The voltage will be a value between 0 and 5 volts, and it will have a fractional part (for example, it might be 2.5 volts), so you'll need to store it inside a **float**. Create a variable named voltage to hold this number. Divide **sensorVal** by 1024.0 and multiply by 5.0. The new number represents the voltage on the pin.

Just like with the sensor value, you'll print this out to the serial monitor.

Convert the voltage to temperature and send the value to the computer

If you examine the sensor's *datasheet*, there is information about the range of the output voltage. Datasheets are like manuals for electronic components. They are written by engineers, for other engineers. The datasheet for this sensor explains that every 10 millivolts of change from the sensor is equivalent to a temperature change of 1 degree Celsius. It also indicates that the sensor can read temperatures below 0 degrees. Because of this, you'll need to create an offset for values below freezing (0 degrees). If you take the voltage, subtract 0.5, and multiply by 100, you get the accurate temperature in degrees Celsius. Store this new number in a floating point variable called temperature.

Now that you have the real temperature, print that out to the serial monitor too. Since the temperature variable is the last thing you're going to be printing out in this loop, you're going to use a slightly different command: **Serial.println( )**. This command will create a new line in the serial monitor after it sends the value. This helps make things easier to read in when they are being printed out.

Turn off LEDs for a low temperature

With the real temperature, you can set up an **if( )...else** statement to light the LEDs. Using the baseline temperature as a starting point, you'll turn on one LED on for every 2 degrees of temperature increase above that baseline. You're going to be looking for a range of values as you move through the temperature scale.

```
14   // convert the ADC reading to voltage
15   float voltage = (sensorVal/1024.0) * 5.0;
```

```
16   Serial.print(", Volts: ");
17   Serial.print(voltage);   .
```

```
18   Serial.print(", degrees C: ");
19   // convert the voltage to temperature in degrees
20   float temperature = (voltage - .5) * 100;
21   Serial.println(temperature);
```

Starter Kit datasheets
arduino.cc/kitdatasheets

```
22   if(temperature < baselineTemp){
23     digitalWrite(2, LOW);
24     digitalWrite(3, LOW);
25     digitalWrite(4, LOW);
```

Turn on one LED for a low
temperature

The && operator means "**and**", in a logical sense. You can check for multiple conditions: "if the temperature is 2 degrees greater than the baseline, and it is less than 4 degrees above the baseline."

Turn on two LEDs for a
medium temperature

If the temperature is between two and four degrees above the baseline, this block of code turns on the LED on pin 3 as well.

Turn on three LEDs for a
high temperature

The Analog-to-Digital Converter can only read so fast, so you should put a small delay at the very end of your **loop( )**. If you read from it too frequently, your values will appear erratic.

USE IT

With the code uploaded to the Arduino, click the serial monitor icon. You should see a stream of values coming out, formatted like this : **Sensor: 200, Volts: .70, degrees C: 17**

Try putting your fingers around the sensor while it is plugged into the breadboard and see what happens to the values in the serial monitor. Make a note of what the temperature is when the sensor is left in the open air.

Close the serial monitor and change the baselineTemp constant in your program to the value you observed the temperature to be. Upload your code again, and try holding the sensor in your fingers. As the temperature rises, you should see the LEDs turn on one by one. Congratulations, hot stuff!

```
26    }else if(temperature >= baselineTemp+2 &&
         temperature < baselineTemp+4){
27       digitalWrite(2, HIGH);
28       digitalWrite(3, LOW);
29       digitalWrite(4, LOW);

30    }else if(temperature >= baselineTemp+4 &&
         temperature < baselineTemp+6){
31       digitalWrite(2, HIGH);
32       digitalWrite(3, HIGH);
33       digitalWrite(4, LOW);

34    }else if(temperature >= baselineTemp+6){
35       digitalWrite(2, HIGH);
36       digitalWrite(3, HIGH);
37       digitalWrite(4, HIGH);

38    }
39    delay(1);
40 }
```

 Create an interface for two people to test their compatibility with each other. You get to decide what compatibility means, and how you'll sense it. Perhaps they have to hold hands and generate heat? Maybe they have to hug? What do you think?

Expanding the types of inputs you can read, you've used analogRead() and the serial monitor to track changes inside your Arduino. Now it's possible to read a large number of analog sensors and inputs.

Ø4

LED

220 OHM RESISTOR

10 KILOHM RESISTOR

PHOTOTRANSISTOR

GEL

INGREDIENTS

COLOR MIXING LAMP

USING A TRI-COLOR LED AND THREE PHOTOTRANSISTORS,
YOU'LL CREATE A LAMP THAT SMOOTHLY CHANGES COLORS
DEPENDING ON EXTERNAL LIGHTING CONDITIONS

Discover: analog output, mapping values

Time: **45 MINUTES**

Level: ■ ■ ■ ■ ■

Builds on projects: **1, 2, 3**

Blinking LEDs can be fun, but what about fading them, or mixing colors?
You might expect that it's just a matter of providing less voltage to an LED to get
it to fade.

The Arduino can't vary the output voltage on its pins, it can only output 5V. Hence you'll need to use a technique called *Pulse Width Modulation (PWM)* to fade LEDs. PWM rapidly turns the output pin high and low over a fixed period of time. The change happens faster than the human eye can see. It's similar to the way movies work, quickly flashing a number of still images to create the illusion of motion.

When you're rapidly turning the pin **HIGH** and **LOW**, it's as if you were changing the voltage. The percentage of time a pin is **HIGH** in a period is called *duty cycle*. When the pin is **HIGH** for half of the period and **LOW** for the other half, the duty cycle is 50%. A lower duty cycle gives you a dimmer LED than a higher duty cycle.

The Arduino Uno has six pins set aside for PWM *(digital pins 3, 5, 6, 9, 10, and 11)*, they can be identified by the ~ next to their number on the board.

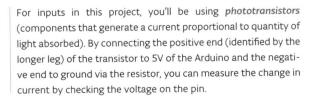

For inputs in this project, you'll be using *phototransistors* (components that generate a current proportional to quantity of light absorbed). By connecting the positive end (identified by the longer leg) of the transistor to 5V of the Arduino and the negative end to ground via the resistor, you can measure the change in current by checking the voltage on the pin.

BUILD THE
CIRCUIT

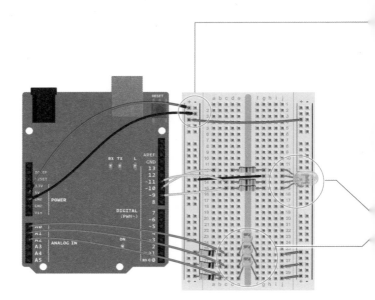

Fig. 1

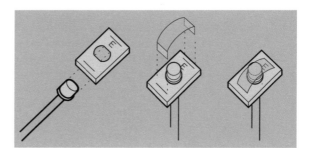

Fig. 2

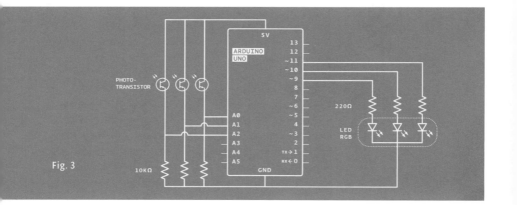

Fig. 3

①   Wire up your breadboard so you have power and ground on both sides, just like the earlier projects.

②   Place the three phototransistors on the breadboard so they cross the center divide from one side to the other, as shown in Fig. 1. Like LEDs phototransistors are polarized components, which means they only allow electricity to flow through them in one direction, so attach the long end of each phototransistor to power. On the other side, attach a 10 kilohm resistor to ground. This resistor is in series with the phototransistor. The phototransistor will force a current to flow in the resistor leading to a voltage drop across it. On the same side as the resistor, connect the phototransistor to Analog In pins 0, 1, and 2 with hookup wire.

③   Take the three colored gels and place one over each of the phototransistors. Place the red gel over the phototransistor connected to A0, the green over the one connected to A1, and the blue over the one connected to A2. Each of these filters lets only light of a specific wavelength through to the sensor it's covering. The red filter passes only red light, the green filter passes only green light, and the blue filter passes only blue light. This allows you to detect the relative color levels in the light that hits your sensors.

④   The LED with 4 legs is a common cathode RGB LED. The LED has separate red, green, and blue elements inside, and one common ground (the cathode). By creating a voltage difference between the cathode and the voltage coming out of the Arduino's PWM pins (which are connected to the anodes through 220-ohm resistors), you'll cause the LED to fade between its three colors. Make note of what the longest pin is on the LED, place it in your breadboard, and connect that pin to ground. Connect the other three pins to digital pins 9, 10 and 11 in series with 220-ohm resistors. Be sure to connect each LED lead to the correct PWM pin, according to the figure on the left.

THE CODE

Useful constants	Set up constants for the pins you're using for input and output, so you can keep track of which sensor pairs with which color on the LED. Use const int for the datatype.
Variables to store the sensor readings as well as the light level of each LED	Add variables for the incoming sensor values and for the output values you'll be using to fade the LED. You can use the **int** datatype for all the variables.
Setting the direction of the digital pins and setting up the serial port	In the **setup( )**, begin serial communication at 9600 bps. Just like in the previous example, you will use this to see the values of the sensors in the serial monitor. Additionally, you will be able to see the mapped values you'll use to fade the LED. Also, define the LED pins as outputs with **pinMode( )**.
Reading the value of each light sensor	In the **loop( )** read the sensor values on A0, A1, and A2 with **analogRead( )** and store the value in the appropriate variables. Put a small **delay( )** between each **analogRead( )** as the ADC takes a millisecond to do its work.
Report the sensor readings to the computer	Print out the sensor values on one line. The "**\t**" is the equivalent of pressing the "**tab**" key on the keyboard.

```
1  const int greenLEDPin = 9;
2  const int redLEDPin = 11;
3  const int blueLEDPin = 10;

4  const int redSensorPin = A0;
5  const int greenSensorPin = A1;
6  const int blueSensorPin = A2;


7  int redValue = 0;
8  int greenValue = 0;
9  int blueValue = 0;

10 int redSensorValue = 0;
11 int greenSensorValue = 0;
12 int blueSensorValue = 0;


13 void setup() {
14   Serial.begin(9600);

15   pinMode(greenLEDPin,OUTPUT);
16   pinMode(redLEDPin,OUTPUT);
17   pinMode(blueLEDPin,OUTPUT);
18 }


19 void loop() {
20   redSensorValue = analogRead(redSensorPin);
21   delay(5);
22   greenSensorValue = analogRead(greenSensorPin);
23   delay(5);
24   blueSensorValue = analogRead(blueSensorPin);

25   Serial.print("Raw Sensor Values \t Red: ");
26   Serial.print(redSensorValue);
27   Serial.print("\t Green: ");
28   Serial.print(greenSensorValue);
29   Serial.print("\t Blue: ");
30   Serial.println(blueSensorValue);
```

Converting the sensor readings

The function to change the LED's brightness via PWM is called `analogWrite()`. It needs two arguments: the pin to write to, and a value between 0-255. This second number represents the duty cycle the Arduino will output on the specified pin. A value of 255 will set the pin **HIGH** all the time, making the attached LED as bright as it can be. A value of 127 will set the pin **HIGH** half the time of the period, making the LED dimmer. 0 would set the pin **LOW** all the time, turning the LED off. To convert the sensor reading from a value between 0-1023 to a value between 0-255 for `analogWrite()`, divide the sensor reading by 4.

Report the calculated LED light levels

Print out the new mapped values on their own line.

Set the LED light levels

USE IT

Once you have your Arduino programmed and wired up, open the serial monitor. The LED will probably be an off-white color, depending on the predominant color of the light in your room. Look at the values coming from the sensors in the serial monitor, if you're in an environment with stable lighting, the number should probably be fairly consistent.

Turn off the light in the room you're in and see what happens to the values of the sensors. With a flashlight, illuminate each of the sensors individually and notice how the values change in the serial monitor, and notice how the LED's color changes. When the photoresistors are covered with a gel, they only react to light of a certain wavelength. This will give you the opportunity to change each of the colors independently.

```
31   redValue = redSensorValue/4;
32   greenValue = greenSensorValue/4;
33   blueValue = blueSensorValue/4;
```

```
34   Serial.print("Mapped Sensor Values \t Red: ");
35   Serial.print(redValue);
36   Serial.print("\t Green: ");
37   Serial.print(greenValue);
38   Serial.print("\t Blue: ");
39   Serial.println(blueValue);
```

```
40   analogWrite(redLEDPin, redValue);
41   analogWrite(greenLEDPin, greenValue);
42   analogWrite(blueLEDPin, blueValue);
43 }
```

You may notice that the photoresistor's output doesn't range all the way from 0 to 1023. That's okay for this project, but for a more detailed explanation of how to calibrate for the range you're reading, see Project 6.

You'll probably notice that the LED's fading is not linear. When the LED is about at half brightness, it appears to stop getting much brighter. This is because our eyes don't perceive brightness linearly. The brightness of the light depends not only on the level that you **analogWrite()** but also on the distance of the light from the diffuser, the distance of your eye from the light, and the brightness of the light relative to other light in the room.

How could you use this to let you know if it's a nice day outside while you're working inside? What other sorts of sensors can you use to control the LED's color?

The LED on its own is pretty neat, but it's not much of a lamp. However, there are a number of different ways you can diffuse the light to make it resemble something like a traditional incandescent. A ping pong ball with a hole cut out for the LED to slide into makes for a nice diffuser. Other ways include covering the light in translucent glue, or sanding the surface of the light. No matter what route you take, you're going to lose at least a little brightness when it's diffused, but it will probably look a lot nicer.

No longer limited to just turning lights on and off, you now have control over how bright or dim something will be. analogWrite() is the function that allows you to PWM components attached to pins 3, 5, 6, 9, 10, or 11, varying the duty cycle.

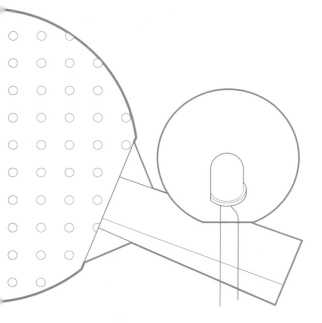

The ping pong ball cut in order to accommodate the LED.

Fig. 4

Ø5

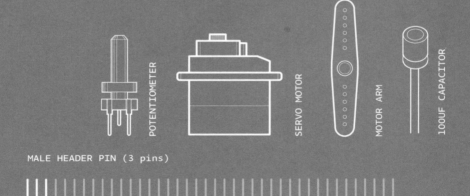

POTENTIOMETER

SERVO MOTOR

MOTOR ARM

100UF CAPACITOR

MALE HEADER PIN (3 pins)

INGREDIENTS

MOOD CUE

USE A SERVO MOTOR TO MAKE A MECHANICAL GAUGE TO
POINT OUT WHAT SORT OF MOOD YOU'RE IN THAT DAY

| Discover: mapping values, servo motors, using built-in libraries

Time: **1 HOUR** | Builds on projects: **1, 2, 3, 4**
Level: ■ ■ ■ ■ ■

Servo motors are special types of motors that don't spin around in a circle, but move to a specific position and stay there until you tell them to move again. Servos usually only rotate 180 degrees (one half of a circle). Combining one of these motors with a little cardboard craft, you'll be able to let people know if they should come and ask for your help on their next project or not.

Similar to the way you used pulses to PWM an LED in the Color Mixing Lamp Project, servo motors expect a number of pulses that tell them what angle to move to. The pulses always come at the same time intervals, but the width varies between 1000 and 2000 microseconds. While it's possible to write code to generate these pulses, the Arduino software comes with a library that allows you to easily control the motor.

Because the servo only rotates 180 degrees, and your analog input goes from 0-1023, you'll need to use a function called **map( )** to change the scale of the values coming from the potentiometer.

One of the great things about the Arduino community are the talented people who extend its functionality through additional software. It's possible for anyone to write libraries to extend the Arduino's functionality. There are libraries for a wide variety of sensors and actuators and other devices that users have contributed to the community. A software library expands the functionality of a programming environment. The Arduino software comes with a number of libraries that are useful for working with hardware or data. One of the included libraries is designed to use with servo motors. In your code, you'll import the library, and all of its functionality will be available to you.

BUILD THE CIRCUIT

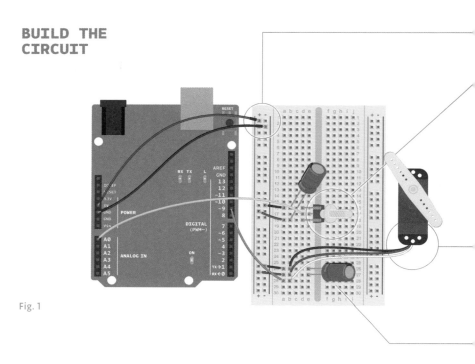

Fig. 1

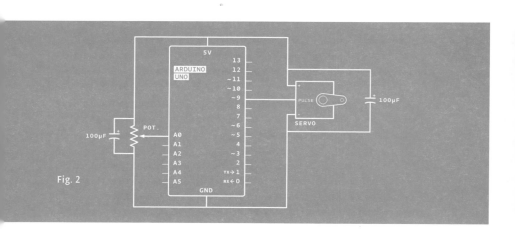

Fig. 2

① Attach 5V and ground to one side of your breadboard from the Arduino.

② Place a potentiometer on the breadboard, and connect one side to 5V, and the other to ground. A potentiometer is a type of voltage divider. As you turn the knob, you change the ratio of the voltage between the middle pin and power. You can read this change on an analog input. Connect the middle pin to analog pin 0. This will control the position of your servo motor.

③ The servo has three wires coming out of it. One is power (red), one is ground (black), and the third (white) is the control line that will receive information from the Arduino. Plug three male headers into the female ends of the servo wires (see Fig. 3). Connect the headers to your breadboard so that each pin is in a different row. Connect 5V to the red wire, ground to the black wire, and the white wire to pin 9.

④ When a servo motor starts to move, it draws more current than if it were already in motion. This will cause a dip in the voltage on your board. By placing a 100uf capacitor across power and ground right next to the male headers as shown in Fig. 1, you can smooth out any voltage changes that may occur. You can also place a capacitor across the power and ground going into your potentiometer. These are called *decoupling capacitors* because they reduce, or decouple, changes caused by the components from the rest of the circuit. Be very careful to make sure you are connecting the cathode to ground (that's the side with a black stripe down the side) and the anode to power. If you put the capacitors in backwards, they can explode.

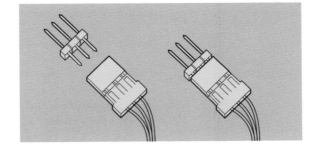

Your servo motor comes with female connectors, so you'll need to add header pins to connect it to the breadboard.

Fig. 3

THE CODE

Import the library	To use the servo library, you'll first need to import it. This makes the additions from the library available to your sketch.
Creating the Servo object	To refer to the servo, you're going to need to create a named instance of the servo library in a variable. This is called an *object*. When you do this, you're making a unique name that will have all the functions and capabilities that the servo library offers. From this point on in the program, every time you refer to my**Servo**, you'll be talking to the servo object.
Variable declaration	Set up a named constant for the pin the potentiometer is attached to, and variables to hold the analog input value and angle you want the servo to move to.
Associating the Servo object with the Arduino pin, initializing the serial port	In the **setup()**, you're going to need to tell the Arduino what pin your servo is attached to. Include a serial connection so you can check the values from the potentiometer and see how they map to angles on the servo motor.
Reading the potentiometer value	In the **loop()**, read the analog input and print out the value to the serial monitor.
Mapping potentiometer value to the servo values	To create a usable value for the servo motor from your analog input, it's easiest to use the **map()** function. This handy function scales numbers for you. In this **case** it will change values between 0-1023 to values between 0-179. It takes five arguments : the number to be scaled (here it's potVal), the minimum value of the input (0), the maximum value of the input (1023), the minimum value of the output (0), and the maximum value of the output (179). Store this new value in the angle variable. Then, print out the mapped value to the serial monitor.
Rotating the servo	Finally, it's time to move the servo. The command **servo. write()** moves the motor to the angle you specify. At the end of the **loop()** put a delay so the servo has time to move to its new position.

Note that #include instructions have not semicolon at the end of the line.

```
1  #include <Servo.h>

2  Servo myServo;

3  int const potPin = A0;
4  int potVal;
5  int angle;

6  void setup() {
7    myServo.attach(9);

8    Serial.begin(9600);
9  }

10 void loop() {
11   potVal = analogRead(potPin);
12   Serial.print("potVal: ");
13   Serial.print(potVal);

14   angle = map(potVal, 0, 1023, 0, 179);
15   Serial.print(", angle: ");
16   Serial.println(angle);

17   myServo.write(angle);
18   delay(15);
19 }
```

USE IT

Once your Arduino has been programmed and powered up, open the serial monitor. You should see a stream of values similar to this:

```
potVal : 1023, angle : 179
potVal : 1023, angle : 179
```

When you turn the potentiometer, you should see the numbers change. More importantly, you should see your servo motor move to a new position. Notice the relationship between the value of potVal and angle in the serial monitor and the position of the servo. You should see consistent results as you turn the pot.

One nice thing about using potentiometers as analog inputs is that they will give you a full range of values between 0 and 1023. This makes them helpful in testing projects that use analog input.

Servo motors are regular motors with a number of gears and some circuits inside. The mechanics inside provide feedback to the circuit, so it is always aware of its position. While it may seem like this is a limited range of motion, it's possible to get it to make a wide variety of different kinds of movements with some additional mechanics. There are a number of resources that describe mechanisms in detail like *robives.com/mechs* and the book *Making Things Move* by **Dustyn Roberts**.

The potentiometer is not the only sensor you can use for controlling the servo. Using the same physical setup (an arrow pointing to a number of different indicators) and a different sensor, what sort of indicator can you make? How would this work with temperature (like in the Love-o-Meter)? Could you tell the time of day with a photoresistor? How does mapping values come into play with those types of sensors?

Servo motors can easily be controlled by the Arduino using a library, which is a collection of code that extends a programming environment. Sometimes it is necessary to repurpose values by mapping them from one scale to another.

Now that you're up and running with motion, it's time to let people know if you're available to help them on their projects, or if you want to be left alone to plan your next creation.

With scissors, cut out a piece of cardboard in the shape of an arrow. Position your servo to 90 degrees (check the angle value in the serial monitor if you're unsure). Tape the arrow so it's oriented in the same direction as the motor's body. Now you should be able to rotate the arrow 180 degrees when turning the potentiometer. Take a piece of paper that is larger than the servo with the arrow attached and draw a half circle on it. On one end of the circle, write "Stay Out". On the other end, write "Come in". Put "Knock please!" in the middle of the arc. Place the servo with the arrow on top of the paper. Congratulations, you've got a way to tell people just how busy you are with your projects!

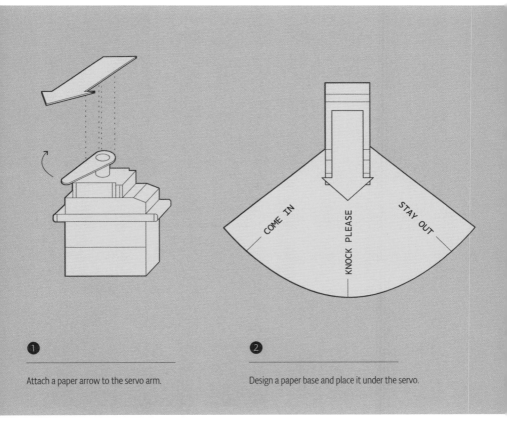

① Attach a paper arrow to the servo arm.

② Design a paper base and place it under the servo.

Ø6

PIEZO

PHOTOTRANSISTOR

10 KILOHM RESISTOR

INGREDIENTS

LIGHT THEREMIN

TIME TO MAKE SOME NOISE! USING A PHOTOTRANSISTOR
AND A PIEZO ELEMENT, YOU'RE GOING TO MAKE A
LIGHT-BASED THEREMIN

> *Discover: making sound with the tone() function, calibrating*
> *analog sensors*
> Time: **45 MINUTES**   Builds on projects: **1, 2, 3, 4**
> Level: ■ ■ ■ ■ ▣

A *theremin* is an instrument that makes sounds based on the movements of
a musician's hands around the instrument. You've probably heard one in scary
movies. The theremin detects where a performer's hands are in relation to two
antennas by reading the capacitive change on the antennas. These antennas are
connected to analog circuitry that create the sound. One antenna controls the
frequency of the sound and the other controls volume. While the Arduino can't
exactly replicate the mysterious sounds from this instrument, it is possible to
emulate them using the **tone()** function. Fig. 1 shows the difference between
the pulses emitted by **analogWrite()** and **tone()**. This enables a transducer
like a speaker or piezo to move back and forth at different speeds.

Notice how the signal is low most of the time, but the frequency is the same as PWM 200.

Notice how the voltage is high most of the time, but the frequency is the same as PWM 50.

The duty cycle is 50% (on half the time, off half the time), but the frequency changes.

Same duty cycle as Tone 440; but twice the frequency.

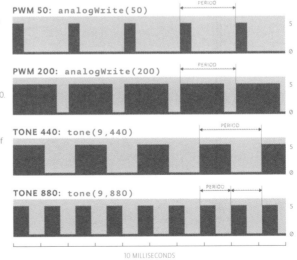

Fig. 1

10 MILLISECONDS

Instead of sensing capacitance with the Arduino, you'll be using a photoresistor to detect the amount of light. By moving your hands over the sensor, you'll change the amount of light that falls on the photoresistor's face, as you did in Project 4. The change in the voltage on the analog pin will determine what frequency note to play.

You'll connect the photoresistors to the Arduino using a voltage divider circuit like you did in Project 4. You probably noticed in the earlier project that when you read this circuit using **analogRead( )**, your readings didn't range all the way from 0 to 1023. The fixed resistor connecting to ground limits the low end of the range, and the brightness of your light limits the high end. Instead of settling for a limited range, you'll calibrate the sensor readings getting the high and low values, mapping them to sound frequencies using the **map( )** function to get as much range out of your theremin as possible. This will have the added benefit of adjusting the sensor readings whenever you move your circuit to a new environment, like a room with different light conditions.

A *piezo* is a small element that vibrates when it receives electricity. When it moves, it displaces air around it, creating sound waves.

BUILD THE CIRCUIT

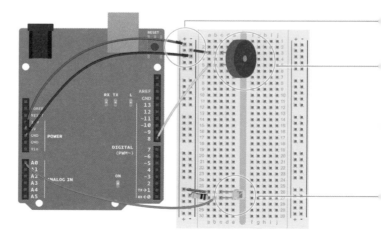

Fig. 2

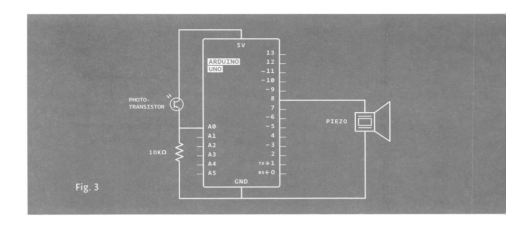

Fig. 3

Traditional theremins can control the frequency and the volume of sound. In this example, You'll be able to control the frequency only. While you can't control the volume through the Arduino, it is possible to change the voltage level that gets to the speaker manually. What happens if you put a potentiometer in series with pin 8 and the piezo? What about another phototransistor?

1 On your breadboard, connect the outer bus lines to power and ground.

2 Take your piezo, and connect one end to ground, and the other to digital pin 8 on the Arduino.

3 Place your phototransistor on the breadboard, connecting the long end to 5V. Connect the other end to the Arduino's analog In pin 0, and to ground through a 10 kilohm resistor.

THE CODE

Create variables for calibrating the sensor

Create a variable to hold the **analogRead( )** value from the photoresistor. Next, create variables for the high and low values. You're going to set the initial value in the sensorLow variable to 1023, and set the value of the **sensorHigh** variable to 0. When you first run the program, you'll compare these numbers to the sensor's readings to find the real maximum and minimum values.

Name a constant for your calibration indicator

Create a constant named **ledPin**. You'll use this as an indicator that your sensor has finished calibrating. For this project, use the on-board LED connected to pin 13.

Set digital pin direction and turn it high

In the **setup( )**, change the **pinMode( )** of ledPin to **OUTPUT**, and turn the light on.

Use a while() loop for calibration

The next steps will calibrate the sensor's maximum and minimum values. You'll use a **while( )** statement to run a loop for 5 seconds. **while( )** loops run until a certain condition is met. In this case you're going to use the **millis( )** function to check the current time. **millis( )** reports how long the Arduino has been running since it was last powered on or reset.

Compare sensor values for calibration

In the loop, you'll read the value of the sensor; if the value is less than **sensorLow** (initially 1023), you'll update that variable. If it is greater than **sensorHigh** (initially 0), that gets updated.

Indicate calibration has finished

When 5 seconds have passed, the while() loop will end. Turn off the LED attached to pin 13. You'll use the sensor high and low values just recorded to scale the frequency in the main part of your program.

```
1  int sensorValue;
2  int sensorLow = 1023;
3  int sensorHigh = 0;
```

```
4  const int ledPin = 13;
```

```
5  void setup() {
```

```
6    pinMode(ledPin, OUTPUT);
7    digitalWrite(ledPin, HIGH);
```

```
8    while (millis() < 5000) {
```

while()
arduino.cc/while

```
9      sensorValue = analogRead(A0);
10     if (sensorValue > sensorHigh) {
11       sensorHigh = sensorValue;
12     }
13     if (sensorValue < sensorLow) {
14       sensorLow = sensorValue;
15     }
16   }
```

```
17   digitalWrite(ledPin, LOW);
18 }
```

Read and store the sensor value	In the **loop( )**, read the value on A0 and store it in **sensorValue**.
Map the sensor value to a frequency	Create a variable named **pitch**. The value of **pitch** is going to be mapped from **sensorValue**. Use **sensorLow** and **sensorHigh** as the bounds for the incoming values. For starting values for output, try 50 to 4000. These numbers set the range of frequencies the Arduino will generate.
Play the frequency	Next, call the **tone( )** function to play a sound. It takes three arguments : what pin to play the sound on (in this case pin 8), what frequency to play (determined by the **pitch** variable), and how long to play the note (try 20 milliseconds to start).
	Then, call a **delay( )** for 10 milliseconds to give the sound some time to play.

USE IT

When you first power the Arduino on, there is a 5 second window for you to calibrate the sensor. To do this, move your hand up and down over the photoresistor, changing the amount of light that reaches it. The closer you replicate the motions you expect to use while playing the instrument, the better the calibration will be.

After 5 seconds, the calibration will be complete, and the LED on the Arduino will turn off. When this happens, you should hear some noise coming from the piezo! As the amount of light that falls on the sensor changes, so should the frequency that the piezo plays.

```
19 void loop() {
20   sensorValue = analogRead(A0);

21   int pitch =
       map(sensorValue,sensorLow,sensorHigh, 50, 4000);



22   tone(8,pitch,20);




23   delay(10);
24 }
```

The range in the **map( )** function that determines the **pitch** is pretty wide, try changing the frequencies to find ones that are the right fit for your musical style.

The **tone( )** function operates very much like the PWM in **analogWrite( )** but with one significant difference. In **analogWrite( )** the frequency is fixed; you change the ratio of the pulses in that period of time to vary the duty cycle. With **tone( )** you're still sending pulses, but changing the frequency of them. **tone( )** always pulses at a 50% duty cycle (half the time the pin is high, the other half the time it is low).

The tone() function gives you the ability to generate different frequencies when it pulses a speaker or piezo. When using sensors in a voltage divider circuit, you probably won't get a full range of values between 0-1023. By calibrating sensors, it's possible to map your inputs to a useable range.

Ø7

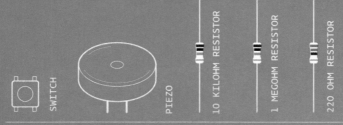

SWITCH

PIEZO

10 KILOHM RESISTOR

1 MEGOHM RESISTOR

220 OHM RESISTOR

INGREDIENTS

KEYBOARD INSTRUMENT

WITH FEW RESISTORS AND BUTTONS YOU ARE GOING TO
BUILD A SMALL MUSICAL KEYBOARD

| Discover: resistor ladders, arrays

| Time: **45 MINUTES** | Builds on projects: **1, 2, 3, 4, 6**
| Level: ■ ■ ■ ■ ▨

*While it's possible to simply hook up a number of momentary switches to digital
inputs to key of different tones, in this project, you'll be constructing something
called a resistor ladder.*

This is a way to read a number of switches using the analog input. It's a helpful
technique if you find yourself short on digital inputs. You'll hook up a number of
switches that are connected in parallel to analog in 0. Most of these will connect
to power through a resistor. When you press each button, a different voltage level
will pass to the input pin. If you press two buttons at the same time, you'll get a
unique input based on the relationship between the two resistors in parallel.

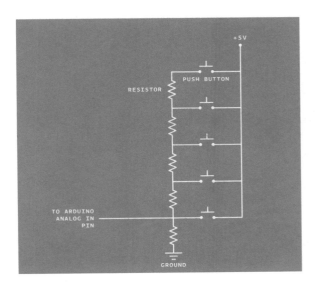

A resistor ladder and five
switches as analog input.
Fig. 1

BUILD THE CIRCUIT

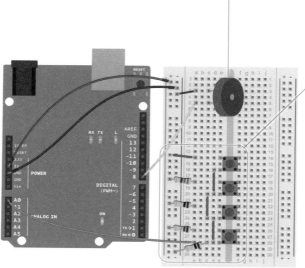

The arrangement of resistors and switches feeding into an analog input is called a resistor ladder.

Fig. 2

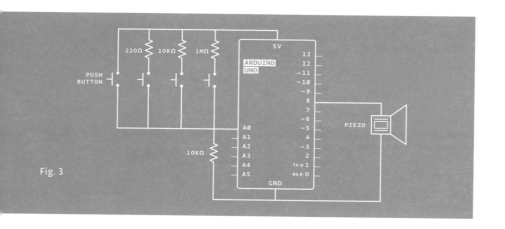

Fig. 3

1. Wire up your breadboard with power and ground as in the previous projects. Connect one end of the piezo to ground. Connect the other end to pin 8 on your Arduino.

2. Place your switches on the breadboard as shown in the circuit. The arrangement of resistors and switches feeding into an analog input is called a resistor ladder. Connect the first one directly to power. Connect the second, third and fourth switches to power through a 220-ohm, 10-kilohm and 1-megohm resistor, respectively. Connect all the switches' outputs together in one junction. Connect this junction to ground with a 10-kilohm resistor, and also connect it to Analog In 0. Each of these acts as a voltage divider.

Think about an enclosure for the keyboard. While old analog synthesizers had wires poking out all over the place, your keyboard is sleek and digital. Prepare a small piece of cardboard that can be cut out to accommodate your buttons. Label the keys, so you know what notes are triggered by each key.

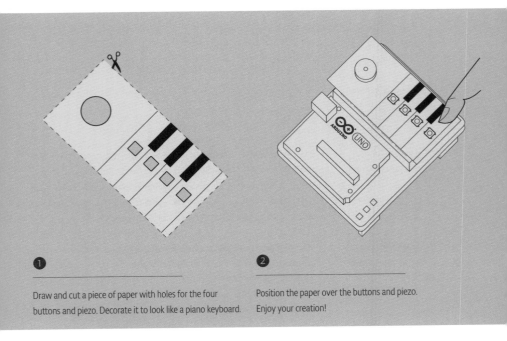

1. Draw and cut a piece of paper with holes for the four buttons and piezo. Decorate it to look like a piano keyboard.

2. Position the paper over the buttons and piezo. Enjoy your creation!

THE CODE

The array

In this program, you'll need to keep a list of frequencies you want to play when you press each of your buttons. You can start out with the frequencies for middle C, D, E and F (262Hz, 294Hz, 330Hz, and 349Hz). To do this, you'll need a new kind of variable called an array.

An array is a way to store different values that are related to each other, like the frequencies in a musical scale, using only one name. They are a convenient tool for you to quickly and efficiently access information. To declare an array, start as you would with a variable, but follow the name with a pair of square brackets: []. After the equals sign, you'll place your elements in curly brackets.

To read or change the elements of the array, you reference the individual element using the array name and then the index of the item you want to address. The index refers to the order in which the items appear when the array is created. The first item in the array is item 0, the second is item 1, and so forth.

Create an array of frequencies

Set up an array of four notes using the frequencies listed above. Make this array a global variable by declaring it before the setup().

Begin serial communication

In your setup(), start serial communication with the computer.

Read the analog value and send it to the serial monitor

In the loop(), declare a local variable to hold the value read on pin A0. Because each switch has a different resistor value connecting it to power, each will have a different value associated with it. To see the values, add the line Serial.println(keyVal) to send to the computer.

Use an if()...else statement to determine what note to play

Using an if()...else statement, you can assign each value to a different tone. The values included in the example program are ballpark figures for these resistor sizes. As all resistors have some tolerance for error, these may not work exactly for you. Use the information from the serial monitor to adjust as necessary.

```
int buttons[6];
// set up an array with 6 integers

int buttons[0] = 2;
// give the first element of the array the value 2
```

```
1 int notes[] = {262,294,330,349};
```

```
2 void setup() {
3   Serial.begin(9600);
4 }
```

```
5 void loop() {
6   int keyVal = analogRead(A0);
7   Serial.println(keyVal);
```

```
8   if(keyVal == 1023){
9     tone(8, notes[0]);
10   }
```

Play the notes that correspond to the analog value

After each **if( )** statement, call the **tone( )** function. The program references the array to determine what frequency to play. If the value of A0 matches one of your if statements, you can tell the Arduino to play a tone. It's possible your circuit is a little "noisy" and the values may fluctuate a little bit while pressing a switch. To accommodate for this variation, it's a good idea to have a small range of values to check against. If you use the comparison "**&&**", you can check multiple statements to see if they are true.

If you press the first button, notes[0] will play. If you press the second, notes[1] will play, and if you press the third, notes[2] will play. This is when arrays become really handy.

Stop playing the tone when nothing is pressed

Only one frequency can play on a pin at any given time, so if you're pressing multiple keys, you'll only hear one sound.

To stop playing notes when there is no button being pressed, call the **noTone( )** function, providing the pin number to stop playing sound on.

USE IT

If your resistors are close in value to the values in the example program, you should hear some sounds from the piezo when you press the buttons. If not, check the serial monitor to make sure each of the buttons is in a range that corresponds to the notes in the **if( )...else** statement. If you're hearing a sound that seems to stutter, try increasing the range a little bit.

Press multiple buttons at the same time, and see what sort of values you get in the serial monitor. Use these new values to trigger even more sounds. Experiment with different frequencies to expand your musical output. You can find frequencies of musical notes on this page: *arduino.cc/en/frequencies*

If you replace the switches and resistor ladder with analog sensors, can you use the additional information they give you to create a more dynamic instrument? You could use the value to change the duration of a note or, like in the Theremin Project, create a sliding scale of sounds.

```
11   else if(keyVal >= 990 && keyVal <= 1010){
12      tone(8, notes[1]);
13   }
14   else if(keyVal >= 505 && keyVal <= 515){
15      tone(8, notes[2]);
16   }
17   else if(keyVal >= 5 && keyVal <= 10){
18      tone(8, notes[3]);
19   }
```

```
20   else{
21      noTone(8);
22   }
23 }
```

The **tone( )** function is fun for generating sounds, but it does have a few limitations. It can only create square waves, not smooth sine waves or triangles. Square waves don't look much like waves at all. As you saw in Fig. 1 in Project 6, it's a series of on and off pulses.

As you start your band, keep some things in mind : only one tone can play at a time and **tone( )** will interfere with **analogWrite( )** on pins 3 and 11.

Arrays are useful for grouping similar types of information together; they are accessed by index numbers which refer to individual elements. Resistor ladders are an easy way to get more digital inputs into a system by plugging into an analog input.

08

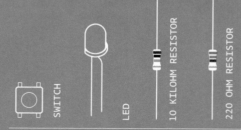

SWITCH

LED

10 KILOHM RESISTOR

220 OHM RESISTOR

INGREDIENTS

DIGITAL HOURGLASS

IN THIS PROJECT, YOU'LL BUILD A DIGITAL HOURGLASS THAT TURNS ON AN LED EVERY TEN MINUTES. KNOW HOW LONG YOU'RE WORKING ON YOUR PROJECTS BY USING THE ARDUINO'S BUILT-IN TIMER

| Discover: long data type, creating a timer

Time: **30 MINUTES** | Builds on projects: **1, 2, 3, 4**
Level: ■ ■ ■ ▪ ▪

Up to now, when you've wanted something to happen at a specific time interval with the Arduino, you've used delay(). This is handy, but a little confining. When the Arduino calls delay(), it freezes its current state for the duration of the delay. That means there can be no other input or output while it's waiting. Delays are also not very helpful for keeping track of time. If you wanted to do something every 10 seconds, having a 10 second delay would be fairly cumbersome.

The millis() function helps to solve these problems. It keeps track of the time your Arduino has been running in milliseconds. You used it previously in Project 6 when you created a timer for calibration.

So far you've been declaring variables as int. An int (integer) is a 16-bit number, it holds values between -32,768 and 32,767. Those may be some large numbers, but if the Arduino is counting 1000 times a second with millis(), you'd run out of space in less than a minute. The long datatype holds a 32-bit number (between -2,147,483,648 and 2,147,483,647). Since you can't run time backwards to get negative numbers, the variable to store millis() time is called an **unsigned long**. When a datatype is called *unsigned*, it is only positive. This allows you to count even higher. An **unsigned long** can count up to 4,294,967,295. That's enough space for millis() to store time for almost 50 days. By comparing the current millis() to a specific value, you can see if a certain amount of time has passed.

When you turn your hourglass over, a tilt switch will change its state, and that will set off another cycle of LEDs turning on.

The tilt switch works just like a regular switch in that it is an on/off sensor. You'll use it here as a digital input. What makes tilt switches unique is that they detect orientation. Typically they have a small cavity inside the housing that has a metal ball. When tilted in the proper way, the ball rolls to one side of the cavity and connects the two leads that are in your breadboard, closing the switch.

With six LEDs, your hourglass will run for an hour, just as its name implies.

BUILD THE
CIRCUIT

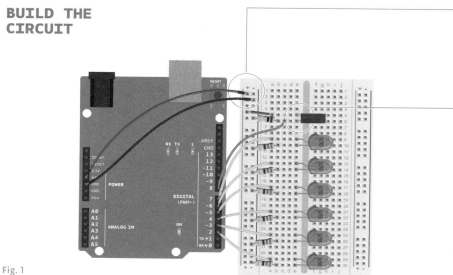

Fig. 1

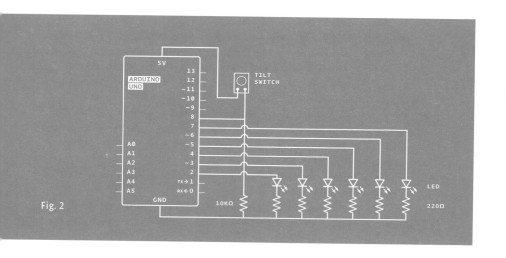

Fig. 2

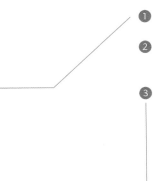

1 Connect power and ground to your breadboard.

2 Connect the anode (longer leg) of six LEDs to digital pins 2-7. Connect the LEDs to ground through 220-ohm resistors.

3 Connect one lead of the tilt switch to 5V. Connect the other to a 10-kilohm resistor to ground. Connect the junction where they meet to digital pin 8.

You don't need to have your Arduino tethered to the computer for this to work. Try building a stand with some cardboard or styrofoam and power the Arduino with a battery to make a portable version. You can create a cover with some numeric indicators alongside the lights.

Tilt switches are great, inexpensive tools for determining the orientation of something. *Accelerometers* are another type of tilt sensor, but they give out much more information. They are also significantly more expensive. If you're just looking to see if something is up or down, a tilt sensor works great.

THE CODE

Declare a named constant	You're going to need a number of global variables in your program to get this all working. To start, create a constant named switchPin. This will be the name of the pin your tilt switch is on.
Create a variable to hold the time	Create a variable of type **unsigned long**, This will hold the time an LED was last changed.
Name variables for the inputs and outputs	Create a variable for the switch state, and another to hold the previous switch state. You'll use these two to compare the switch's position from one loop to the next.
	Create a variable named led. This will be used to count which LED is the next one to be turned on. Start out with pin 2.
Declare a variable describing the interval between events	The last variable you're creating is going to be the interval between each LED turning on. This will be be a **long** datatype. In 10 minutes (the time between each LED turning on) 600,000 milliseconds pass. If you want the delay between lights to be longer or shorter, this is the number you change.
Set the direction of your digital pins	In your **setup()**, you need to declare the LED pins 2-7 as outputs. A **for()** loop declares all six as **OUTPUT** with just 3 lines of code. You also need to declare switchPin as an **INPUT**.
Check the time since the program started running	When the **loop()** starts, you're going to get the amount of time the Arduino has been running with **millis()** and store it in a local variable named **currentTime**.
Evaluate the amount of time that has passed since the previous loop()	Using an **if()** statement, you'll check to see if enough time has passed to turn on an LED. Subtract the **currentTime** from the **previousTime** and check to see if it is greater than the interval variable. If 600,000 milliseconds have passed (10 minutes), you'll set the variable previousTime to the value of **currentTime**.

```
1 const int switchPin = 8;

2 unsigned long previousTime = 0;

3 int switchState = 0;
4 int prevSwitchState = 0;

5 int led = 2;

6 long interval = 600000;

7 void setup() {
8   for(int x = 2;x<8;x++){
9     pinMode(x, OUTPUT);
10  }

11  pinMode(switchPin, INPUT);
12 }

13 void loop(){
14   unsigned long currentTime = millis();

15   if(currentTime - previousTime > interval) {
16     previousTime = currentTime;
```

Turn on an LED, prepare for the next one	previousTime indicates the last time an LED was turned on. Once you've set previousTime, turn on the LED, and increment the led variable. The next time you pass the time interval, the next LED will light up.
Check to see if all lights are on	Add one more if statement in the program to check if the LED on pin 7 is turned on. Don't do anything with this yet. You'll decide what happens at the end of the hour later.
Read the value of the switch	Now that you've checked the time, you'll want to see if the switch has changed its state. Read the switch value into the switchState variable.
Reset the variables to their defaults if necessary	With an if() statement, check to see if the switch is in a different position than it was previously. The != evaluation checks to see if switchState does not equal prevSwitchState. If they are different, turn the LEDs off, return the led variable to the first pin, and reset the timer for the LEDs by setting previousTime to currentTime.
Set the current state to the previous state	At the end of the loop(), save the switch state in prevSwitchState , so you can compare it to the value you get for switchState in the next loop().

USE IT

Once you've programmed the board, check the time on a clock. After 10 minutes have passed, the first LED should have turned on. Every 10 minutes after that, a new light will turn on. At the end of an hour, all six light should be on. When you flip the circuit over, and cause the tilt switch to change its state, the lights will turn off and the timer will start again.

```
17    digitalWrite(led, HIGH);
18    led++;

19    if(led == 7){
20    }
21  }

22  switchState = digitalRead(switchPin);

23  if(switchState != prevSwitchState){
24    for(int x = 2;x<8;x++){
25      digitalWrite(x, LOW);
26    }

27    led = 2;
28    previousTime = currentTime;
29  }

30  prevSwitchState = switchState;
31 }
```

When the clock reaches one hour and all six lights are on, they just stay on. Can you think of a way to get your attention when the hour is up? Sound or flashing the lights are both good indicators. The led variable can be checked to see if all the lights are on, that's a good place to check for grabbing someone's attention. Unlike an hourglass filled with sand, the lights go either up or down depending on the orientation of the switch. Can you figure out how you can use the switchState variable to indicate what direction the lights should go?

To measure the amount of time between events, use the millis() function. Because the numbers it generates are larger than what you can store in an int, you should use the datatype unsigned long for storing its values.

09

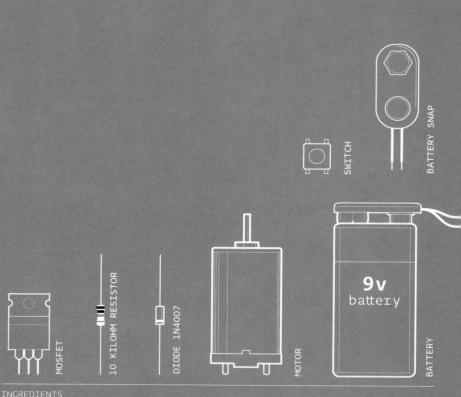

MOSFET

10 KILOHM RESISTOR

DIODE 1N4007

MOTOR

SWITCH

BATTERY SNAP

9v
battery

BATTERY

INGREDIENTS

MOTORIZED PINWHEEL

GET THE ARDUINO TO SPIN A COLORFUL PINWHEEL
USING A MOTOR

Discover: transistors, high current/voltage loads

Time: **45 MINUTES**   Builds on projects: **1, 2, 3, 4**
Level: ■ ■ ■ ■ ■

Controlling motors with an Arduino is more complicated than just controlling LEDs for a couple of reasons. First, motors require more current than the Arduino's output pins can supply, and second, motors can generate their own current through a process called induction, which can damage your circuit if you don't plan for it. However, motors make it possible to move physical things, making your projects much more exciting. They're worth the complications!

Moving things takes a lot of energy. Motors typically require more current than the Arduino can provide. Some motors require a higher voltage as well. To start moving, and when it has a heavy load attached, a motor will draw as much current as it can. The Arduino can only provide 40 milliamps (mA) from its digital pins, much less than what most motors require to work.

Transistors are components that allow you to control high current and high voltage power sources from the low current output of the Arduino. There are many different kinds, but they work on the same principle. You can think of transistors as digital switches. When you provide voltage to one of the transistor's pins, called the gate, it closes the circuit between the other two pins, called the source and drain. This way, you can turn a higher current/voltage motor on and off with your Arduino.

Motors are a type of inductive device. Induction is a process by which a changing electrical current in a wire can generate a changing magnetic field around the wire. When a motor is given electricity, a tightly wound coil inside the housing of copper creates a magnetic field. This field causes the shaft (the part that sticks out of the housing) to spin around.

The reverse is also true: a motor can generate electricity when the shaft is spun around. Try attaching an LED to the two leads of your motor, then spin the shaft with your hand. If nothing happens, spin the shaft the other way. The LED should light up. You've just made a tiny generator out of your motor.

When you stop supplying energy to a motor, it will continue to spin, because it has inertia. When it's spinning, it will generate a voltage in the opposite direction than the current you gave it. You saw this effect when you made your motor light up an LED. This reverse voltage, sometimes called back-voltage, can damage your transistor. For this reason, you should put a diode in parallel with the motor, so that the **back voltage** passes through the diode. The diode will only allow electricity to flow in one direction, protecting the rest of the circuit.

BUILD THE CIRCUIT

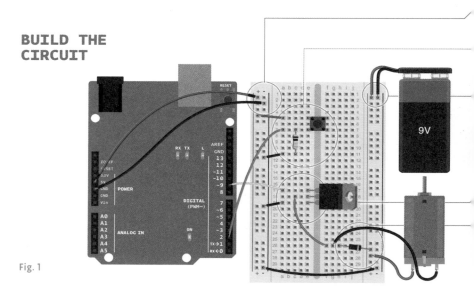

Fig. 1

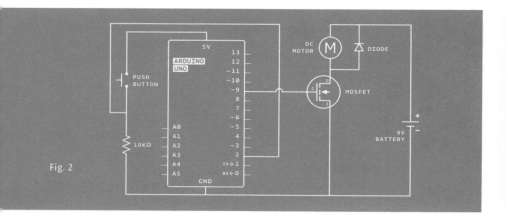

Fig. 2

1. Connect power and ground to your breadboard through the Arduino.

2. Add a momentary switch to the board, connecting one side to power, and the other side to digital pin 2 on the Arduino. Add a 10-kilohm pull-down resistor to ground on the output pin of the switch.

3. When using circuits with different voltages, you have to connect their grounds together to provide a common ground. Plug the 9V battery snap into your breadboard. Connect ground from the battery to ground of your Arduino on the breadboard with a jumper, as shown in Fig. 1. Then attach the motor's free lead to the 9V power.

4. Place the transistor on the board. Look at the component so that the metal tab is facing away from you. Connect digital pin 9 to the left pin on the transistor. This pin is called the **gate**. A change in voltage on the gate makes a connection between the other two pins. Connect one end of the motor to the middle pin of the transistor. This pin is called the **drain**. When the Arduino activates the transistor by supplying voltage to the gate, this pin will be connected to the third pin, called the **source**. Connect the source to ground.

5. Next, connect the motor's voltage supply to the motor and breadboard. The last component to be added is the diode. The diode is a polarized component, it can go only one way in the circuit. Notice that the diode has a stripe on one end. That end is the negative end, or cathode, of the diode. The other end is the positive end, or anode. Connect the anode of the diode to the ground of the motor and the cathode of the diode to the power of the motor. See Fig. 1. This may seem backwards, and in fact, it is. The diode will help prevent any back-voltage generated by the motor from going back into your circuit. Remember, back voltage will flow in the opposite direction of the voltage that you supply.

LEDs are diodes too, in case you were wondering why their leads were also called anodes and cathodes. There are many kinds of diodes, but they all share one trait. They allow current to flow from anode to cathode, but not the reverse.

THE CODE

Name your constants and variables

The code is remarkably similar to the code you first used for turning on an LED. First of all, set up some constants for the switch and motor pins and a variable named **switchState** to hold the value of the switch.

Declare the pins' direction

In your **setup()**, declare the **pinMode()** of the motor (**OUTPUT**) and **switch** (**INPUT**) pins.

Read the input, pull the output high if pressed

Your **loop()** is straightforward. Check the state of the **switchPin** with **digitalRead()**.

If the switch is pressed, turn the motorPin **HIGH**. If it is not pressed, turn the pin **LOW**. When **HIGH**, the transistor will activate, completing the motor circuit. When **LOW**, the motor will not spin.

Motors have an optimal operating voltage. They will work on as little as 50% of the rated voltage and as much as 50% over that number. If you vary the voltage, you can change the speed at which the motor rotates. Don't vary it too much, though, or you will burn out your motor.

Motors require special consideration when being controlled by a microcontroller. Typically the microcontroller cannot provide enough current and/or voltage to power a motor. Because of this, you use transistors to interface between the two. It's also smart to use diodes to prevent damaging your circuit.

```
1 const int switchPin = 2;
2 const int motorPin = 9;
3 int switchState = 0;

4 void setup() {
5   pinMode(motorPin, OUTPUT);
6   pinMode(switchPin, INPUT);
7 }

8 void loop(){
9   switchState = digitalRead(switchPin);

10  if (switchState == HIGH) {
11    digitalWrite(motorPin, HIGH);
12  }
13  else {
14    digitalWrite(motorPin, LOW);
15  }
16 }
```

Transistors are solid state devices, they have no moving parts. Because of this, you can switch them on and off very quickly. Try hooking up a potentiometer to an analog input and use that to PWM the pin that controls the transistor. What do you think will happen to the motor's speed if you vary the voltage it's getting? Using your patterns on your spinner, can you get different visual effects?

USE IT

Assemble the CD hub as shown in step 1, and attach it to the motor as shown in step 2. Attach the die-cut paper pattern to a CD as shown in step 3. Snap the CD to the hub and secure with a drop of glue. Allow to try before proceeding. Plug a 9V battery to your battery snap. Power your Arduino over USB. When you press the switch on the breadboard, the motor will spin very rapidly.

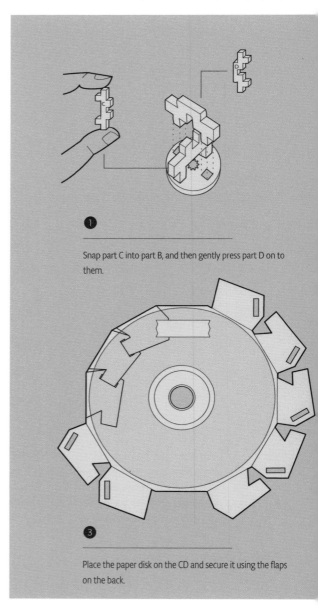

Snap part C into part B, and then gently press part D on to them.

Place the paper disk on the CD and secure it using the flaps on the back.

With the motor spinning as fast as it does, you can probably make a pretty large spinner. Be careful that it doesn't fly off and poke someone in the eye. Experiment with different patterns on the outside to create visual effects.

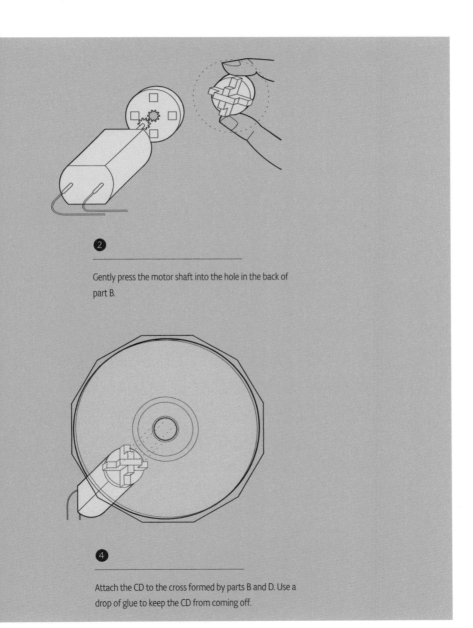

2

Gently press the motor shaft into the hole in the back of part B.

4

Attach the CD to the cross formed by parts B and D. Use a drop of glue to keep the CD from coming off.

10

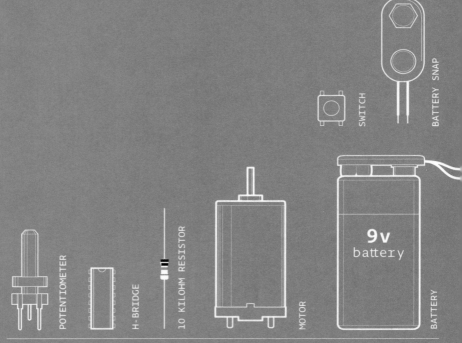

POTENTIOMETER

H-BRIDGE

10 KILOHM RESISTOR

MOTOR

9v battery

BATTERY

SWITCH

BATTERY SNAP

INGREDIENTS

ZOETROPE

CREATE MOVING IMAGES IN FORWARD AND REVERSE WITH
YOUR ARDUINO WHEN YOU CONNECT A MOTOR TO AN
H-BRIDGE AND SOME STILL IMAGES

| Discover: H-bridges

Time: **30 MINUTES** | Builds on projects: **1, 2, 3, 4, 9**
Level: ■ ■ ■ ■ ■

Before the internet, television, even before movies, some of the first moving images were created with a tool called a zoetrope. *Zoetropes create the illusion of motion from a group of still images that have small changes in them. They are typically cylinders with slits cut in the side. When the cylinder spins and you look through the slits, your eyes perceive the still images on the other side of the wall to be animated. The slits help keep the images from becoming a big blur, and the speed at which the images appear provide cause the images to appear to move. Originally, these novelties were spun by hand, or with a cranking mechanism.*

In this project, you'll build your own zoetrope that animates a carnivorous plant. You'll power the motion with a motor. To make this system even more advanced, you'll add a switch that lets you control direction, another to turn it off and on, and a potentiometer to control the speed.

In the Motorized Pinwheel Project you got a motor to spin in one direction. If you were to take power and ground on the motor and flip their orientation, the motor would spin in the opposite direction. It's not very practical to do that everytime you want to spin something in a different direction, so you'll be using a component called an H-bridge to reverse the polarity of the motor.

H-bridges are a type of components known as *integrated circuits (IC)*. ICs are components that hold large circuits in a tiny package. These can help simplify more complex circuits by placing them in an easily replaceable component. For example, the H-bridge you're using in this example has a number of transistors built in. To build the circuit inside the H-bridge you would probably need another breadboard.

Fig. 1

With an IC, you can access the circuits through the pins that come out the sides. Different ICs have different numbers of pins, and not all of them are used in every circuit. It's sometimes convenient to refer to the pins by number instead of function. When looking at an IC, the part with a dimple is referred to as the top . You can identify pin numbers by counting from the top-left in a "U" direction like in Fig. 1.

BUILD THE CIRCUIT

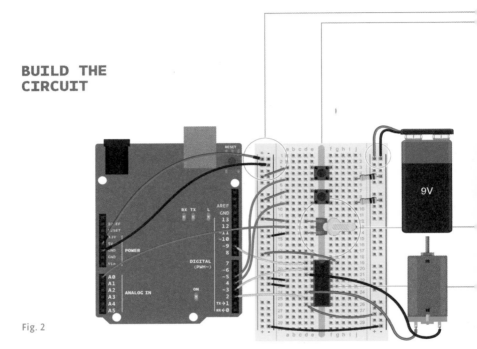

Fig. 2

Fig. 3

1. Connect power and ground from one side of your breadboard to the Arduino.

2. Add 2 momentary switches to the breadboard, connecting one side of each to power. Add a 10Kohm pull-down resistor in series with ground on the output pin of both switches.
The switch on pin 4 will control direction, the switch on pin 5 will turn the motor on and off.

3. Connect the potentiometer to the breadboard. Wire 5V to one side and ground to the other. Attach the center pin to analog input 0 on the Arduino. This will be used to control the speed of the motor.

4. Place the H-bridge on your breadboard so it straddles the center (see Fig. 2 for detail of placement). Connect pin 1 of the H-bridge to digital pin 9 on the Arduino. This is the enable pin on the H-bridge. When it receives 5V, it turns the motor on, when it receives 0V, it turns the motor off. You will use this pin to PWM the H-bridge, and adjust the speed of the motor.

5. Connect pin 2 on the H-bridge to digital pin 3 on the Arduino. Connect pin 7 to digital pin 2. These are the pins you will use to communicate with the H-bridge, telling it which direction to spin. If pin 3 is **LOW** and pin 2 is **HIGH**, the motor will spin in one direction. If pin 2 is **LOW** and pin 3 is **HIGH**, the motor will spin in the opposite direction. If both the pins are **HIGH** or **LOW** at the same time, the motor will stop spinning.

6. The H-bridge get its power from pin 16, plug that into 5V. Pins 4 and 5 both go to ground.

7. Attach your motor to pins 3 and 6 on the H-bridge. These two pins will switch on and off depending on the signals you send to pins 2 and 7.

8. Plug the battery connector (without the battery attached!) to the other power rails on your breadboard. Connect ground from your Arduino to the battery's ground. Connect pin 8 from the H-bridge to the battery power. This is the pin that the H-bridge powers the motor from. Make sure you do not have your 9V and 5V power lines connected. They must be separate, only ground should be connected between the two.

THE CODE

Name your constants

Create constants for the output and input pins.

Create variables for remem-bering program state

Use variables to hold the values from your inputs. You'll be doing state change detection for both switches, comparing the state from one loop to the next, similar to the Hourglass Project. So, in addition to storing the current state, you'll need to record the previous state of each switch.

Create variables for motor control

motorDirection keeps track of which direction the motor is spinning, and **motorPower** keeps track of whether the motor is spinning or not.

Declare the digital pins as inputs and outputs

In **setup()**, set the direction of each input and output pin.

Turn the motor off

Turn the enable pin **LOW** to start, so the motor isn't spinning right away.

Read sensor information

In your **loop()**, read the state of the On/Off switch and store it in the **onOffSwitchState** variable.

```
1  const int controlPin1 = 2;
2  const int controlPin2 = 3;
3  const int enablePin = 9;
4  const int directionSwitchPin = 4;
5  const int onOffSwitchStateSwitchPin = 5;
6  const int potPin = A0;

7  int onOffSwitchState = 0;
8  int previousOnOffSwitchState = 0;
9  int directionSwitchState = 0;
10 int previousDirectionSwitchState = 0;

11 int motorEnabled = 0;
12 int motorSpeed = 0;
13 int motorDirection = 1;

14 void setup(){
15   pinMode(directionSwitchPin, INPUT);
16   pinMode(onOffSwitchStateSwitchPin, INPUT);
17   pinMode(controlPin1, OUTPUT);
18   pinMode(controlPin2, OUTPUT);
19   pinMode(enablePin, OUTPUT);

20   digitalWrite(enablePin, LOW);
21 }

22 void loop(){
23   onOffSwitchState =
        digitalRead(onOffSwitchStateSwitchPin);
24   delay(1);
25   directionSwitchState =
        digitalRead(directionSwitchPin);
26   motorSpeed = analogRead(potPin)/4;
```

Check if on/off sensor has changed	If there is a difference between the current switch state and the previous, and the switch is currently **HIGH**, set the `motorPower` variable to 1. If it is **LOW**, set the variable to 0. Read the values of the direction switch and potentiometer. Store the values in their respective variables.
Check to see if the direction has changed	Check to see if the direction switch is currently in a different position than it was previously. If it is different, change the motor direction variable. There are only 2 ways for the motor to spin, so you'll want to alternate the variable between two states. One way to accomplish this is by using the inversion operator like so: `motorDirection = !motorDirection`.
Change the pins to turn the motor in the proper direction	The motorDirection variable determines which direction the motor is turning. To set the direction, you set the control pins setting one **HIGH** and the other **LOW**. When motorDirection changes, reverse the states of the control pins. If the direction switch gets pressed, you'll want to spin the motor in the other direction by reversing the state of the `controlPins`.
PWM the motor if it is enabled	If the motorEnabled variable is 1, set the speed of the motor using `analogWrite()` to PWM the enable pin. If `motorEnabled` is 0, then turn the motor off by setting the `analogWrite` value to 0.
Save the current states for the next loop()	Before exiting the `loop()`, save the current state of the switches as the previous state for the next run through the program.

```
27   if(onOffSwitchState != previousOnOffSwitchState){
28     if(onOffSwitchState == HIGH){
29       motorEnabled = !motorEnabled;
30     }
31   }
```

```
32   if (directionSwitchState !=
     previousDirectionSwitchState) {
33     if (directionSwitchState == HIGH) {
34       motorDirection = !motorDirection;
35     }
36   }
```

```
37   if (motorDirection == 1) {
38     digitalWrite(controlPin1, HIGH);
39     digitalWrite(controlPin2, LOW);
40   }
```

```
41   else {
42     digitalWrite(controlPin1, LOW);
43     digitalWrite(controlPin2, HIGH);
44   }
```

```
45   if (motorEnabled == 1) {
46     analogWrite(enablePin, motorSpeed);
47   }
48   else {
49     analogWrite(enablePin, 0);
50   }
```

```
51   previousDirectionSwitchState =
       directionSwitchState;
52   previousOnOffSwitchState = onOffSwitchState;
53 }
```

USE IT

Plug your Arduino into your computer. Attach the battery to the connector. When you press the On/Off switch, the motor should start spinning. If you turn the potentiometer, it should speed up and slow down. Pressing the On/Off button another time will stop the motor. Try pressing the direction button and verify the motor spins both ways. Also, if you turn the knob on the pot, you should see the motor speed up or slow down depending on the value it is sending.

Once you've verified that the circuit works as expected, disconnect the battery and USB from the circuit.

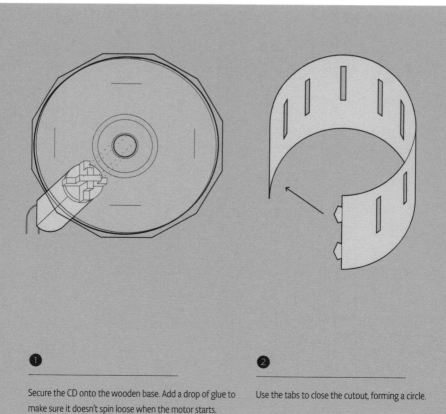

1

Secure the CD onto the wooden base. Add a drop of glue to make sure it doesn't spin loose when the motor starts.

2

Use the tabs to close the cutout, forming a circle.

In order to build your zoetrope, you must take the pinwheel you used in Project 9 and the cutout with the vertical slits that is included in your kit. Once the CD is securely attached to the shaft of the motor, plug everything back in. Hold your project up, so you can look through the slits (but make sure the CD is secured to the motor, and don't get too close to it). You should see the sequence of still images "move"! If it is going too fast or too slow, turn the knob of the potentiometer to adjust the speed of the animation.

Try pressing the direction switch to see what the animation looks like when played backwards. The zoetrope and images provided in the kit are only your starting point: try experimenting with your own animations, using the cutout as a reference.

To do this, start with a basic image. Identify one fixed point in it, and make small changes to the rest in each frame. Try to gradually return to the original image so that you can play the animation in a continuous loop.

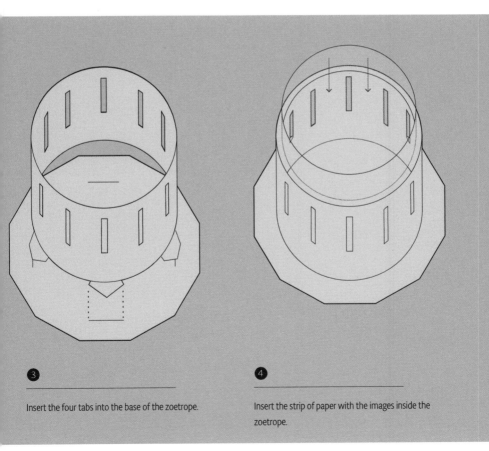

3 Insert the four tabs into the base of the zoetrope.

4 Insert the strip of paper with the images inside the zoetrope.

Zoetropes work because of a phenomena called "persistence of vision", sometimes abbreviated to POV. POV describes the illusion of motion that is created when our eyes observe still images with minor variations in rapid succession. If you search online for "POV display", you'll find many projects made by people that leverage this effect, often with LEDs and an Arduino.

Make a base to support the motor. A small cardboard box with a hole cut in it could work as a base, leaving your hands free to play with the switches and knob. This will make it easier to show off your work to everyone.

With a little work, you can get your zoetrope working in low light situations as well. Hook up an LED and resistor to one of your free digital output pins. Also add a second potentiometer, and connect it to an analog input. Position the light so it shines on the images. Using the analog input to time the flashes of the LED, try and time it so the light flashes when the slit is in front of your eyes. This could take some fiddling with the knobs, but the resulting effect is really spectacular!

11

SWITCH

10 KILOHM RESISTOR

220 OHM RESISTOR

POTENTIOMETER

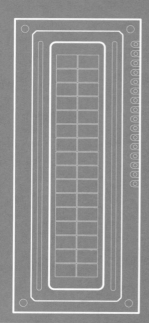

LCD SCREEN

CRYSTAL BALL

CREATE A CRYSTAL BALL TO TELL YOUR FUTURE

| *Discover: LCD displays, switch/case statements, random()*

| Time: **1 HOUR** | Builds on projects: **1, 2, 3**
| Level: ■ ■ ■ ■ ■

Crystal balls can help "predict" the future. You ask a question to the all-knowing ball, and turn it over to reveal an answer. The answers will be predetermined, but you can write in anything you like. You'll use your Arduino to choose from a total of 8 responses. The tilt switch in your kit will help replicate the motion of shaking the ball for answers.

The LCD can be used to display alphanumeric characters. The one in your kit has 16 columns and 2 rows, for a total of 32 characters. There is a large number of connections on the board. These pins are used for power and communication, so it knows what to write on screen, but you won't need to connect all of them. See Fig. 1 for the pins you need to connect.

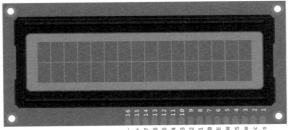

The pins on the LCD screen that are used in the project and labels.

Fig. 1

BUILD THE CIRCUIT

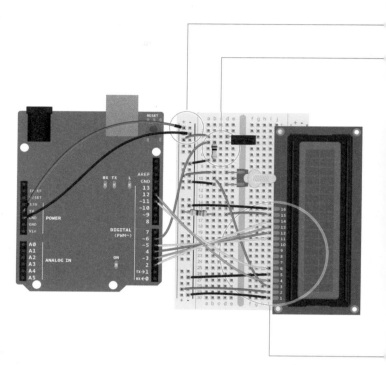

Fig. 2

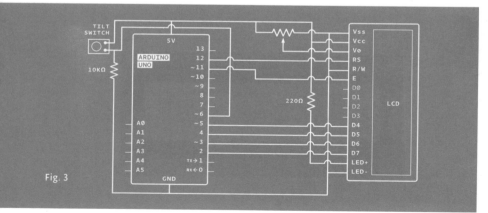

Fig. 3

In this schematic the LCD pins arrangement does not match the physical order depicted in Fig. 2. In a schematic, the pins are rearranged by logical grouping to make the schematic as clear as possible. This is a little confusing to newcomers until you get used to it.

The circuit is not overly complex, but there is a lot of wires. Pay attention when wiring everything up to make sure it's correct.

1. Connect power and ground to one side of your breadboard.

2. Place the tilt switch on the breadboard and attach one lead to 5V. Attach the other side to ground through a 10-kilohm resistor, and to your Arduino's pin 6. You're wiring this as a digital input, just as you've done in several other projects.

3. The register select (**RS**) pin controls where the characters will appear on screen. The read/write pin (**R/W**) puts the screen in read or write mode. You'll be using the write mode in this project. The enable (**EN**) tells the LCD that it will be receiving a command. The data pins (**D0-D7**) are used to send character data to the screen. You'll only be using 4 of these (**D4-D7**). Finally, there's a connection for adjusting the contrast of the display. You'll use a potentiometer to control this.

4. The LiquidCrystal library that comes with the Arduino software handles all the writing to these pins, and simplifies the process of writing software to display characters.
   The two outside pins of the LCD (**Vss** and **LED-**) need to be connected to ground. Also, connect the R/W pin to ground. This places the screen in write mode. The LCD power supply (**Vcc**) should connect directly to 5V. The LED+ pin on the screen connects to power through a 220-ohm resistor.

5. Connect: Arduino Digital pin 2 to LCD **D7**, Arduino Digital pin 3 to LCD **D6**, Arduino Digital pin 4 to LCD **D5**, Arduino Digital pin 5 to LCD **D4**. These are the data pins that tell the screen what character to display.

6. Connect **EN** on the screen to pin 11 on your Arduino. **RS** on the LCD connects to pin 12. This pin enables writing to the LCD.

7. Place the potentiometer on the breadboard, connecting one end pin to power and the other to ground. The center pin should connect to **V0** on the LCD. This will allow you to change the contrast of the screen.

Set up the LiquidCrystal library

First, you'll need to import the **LiquidCrystal** library.
Next, you'll initialize the library, somewhat similar to the way you did with the Servo library, telling it what pins it will be using to communicate.

Now that you've set up the library, it's time to create some variables and constants. Create a constant to hold the pin of the switch pin, a variable for the current state of the switch, a variable for the previous state of the switch, and one more to choose which reply the screen will show.

Print your first line

Set up the switch pin as an input with **pinMode()** in your **setup()**. Start the LCD library, and tell it how large the screen is.

Move the cursor

Now it's time to write a small introductory screen welcoming you to the 8-ball. The **print()** function writes to the LCD screen. You're going to write the words "Ask the" on the top line of the screen. The cursor is automatically at the beginning of the top line.

In order to write to the next line, you'll have to tell the screen where to move the cursor. The coordinates of the first column on the second line are 0,1 (recall that computers are zero indexed. 0,0 is the first column of the first row). Use the function **lcd.setCursor()** to move the cursor to the proper place, and tell it to write "Crystal ball!".

Now, when you start the program, it will say "Ask the Crystal ball!" on your screen.
In the **loop()**, you're going to check the switch first, and put the value in the switchState variable.

Choose a random anwser

Use an **if()** statement to determine if the switch is in a different position than it was previously. If it is different than it was before, and it is currently LOW, then it's time to choose a random reply. The **random()** function returns a number based on the argument you provide. To start, you'll have a total number of 8 different responses for the ball. Whenever the statement random(8) is called, it will give a number between 0-7. Store that number in your reply variable.

```
1 #include <LiquidCrystal.h>
2 LiquidCrystal lcd(12, 11, 5, 4, 3, 2);
```

```
3 const int switchPin = 6;
4 int switchState = 0;
5 int prevSwitchState = 0;
6 int reply;
```

```
7 void setup() {
8   lcd.begin(16, 2);
9   pinMode(switchPin,INPUT);
```

LCD library reference
arduino.cc/lcdlibrary

```
10   lcd.print("Ask the");
```

```
11   lcd.setCursor(0, 1);
12   lcd.print("Crystal Ball!");
13 }
```

```
14 void loop() {
15   switchState = digitalRead(switchPin);
```

```
16   if (switchState != prevSwitchState) {
17     if (switchState == LOW) {
18       reply = random(8);
```

Random reference
arduino.cc/random

Clear the screen with the function `lcd.clear()`. This also moves the cursor back to location 0,0; the first column in the first row of the LCD. Print out the line " The ball says:" and move the cursor for the output.

Predict the future

The `switch()` statement executes different pieces of code depending on the value you give it. Each of these different pieces of code is called a **case**. `switch()` checks the value of the variable reply; whatever value reply holds will determine what named case statement is executed.

Inside the case statements, the code will be the same, but the messages will be different. For example, in case 0 the code says `lcd.print ("Yes")`. After the `lcd.print()` function, there's another command: **break**. It tells the Arduino where the end of the case is. When it hits **break**, it skips to the end of the switch statement. You'll be creating a total of 8 case statements to start out. Four of the responses will be positive, 2 will be negative, and the final 2 will ask you to try again.

The last thing to do in your `loop()` is to assign switchState's value to the variable **prevSwitchState**. This enables you to track changes in the switch the next time the loop runs.

```
19      lcd.clear();
20      lcd.setCursor(0, 0);
21      lcd.print("The ball says:");
22      lcd.setCursor(0, 1);

23      switch(reply){
24        case 0:
25        lcd.print("Yes");
26        break;
27        case 1:
28        lcd.print("Most likely");
29        break;
30        case 2:
31        lcd.print("Certainly");
32        break;
33        case 3:
34        lcd.print("Outlook good");
35        break;
36        case 4:
37        lcd.print("Unsure");
38        break;
39        case 5:
40        lcd.print("Ask again");
41        break;
42        case 6:
43        lcd.print("Doubtful");
44        break;
45        case 7:
46        lcd.print("No");
47        break;
48        }
49      }
50    }

51   prevSwitchState = switchState;
52 }
```

Switch Case reference
arduino.cc/switchcase

USE IT

To use the magic ball, power the Arduino. Check the screen to make sure it says "Ask the Crystal ball!" If you can't see the characters, try turning the potentiometer. It will adjust the contrast of the screen.

Ask a question of your crystal ball, and try tilting the switch upside down and back again. You should get an answer to your question. If the answer doesn't suit you, ask again.

Try adding your own sayings to the **print()** statements, but be mindful of the fact that there are only 16 characters to use per line. You can also try adding more responses. Make sure when you add additional switch cases, you adjust the number of options that will randomly populate the reply variable.

LCDs work by changing the electrical properties of a liquid sandwiched between polarized glass. The glass only allows certain kinds of light to pass through. When the liquid between the glass is charged, it starts to form into a semi-solid state. This new state runs in a different direction than the polarized glass, blocking light from passing through, thus creating the characters you see on the screen.

The functions covered here for changing the LCD screen's text are fairly simple. Once you have a handle on how it works, look at some of the other functions the library has. Try getting text to scroll, or continually update. To find out more about how the LiquidCrystal library works, visit: *arduino.cc/lcd*

An LCD display enables you to show text on a screen, using the LiquidCrystal library. With a switch...case statements control the flow of programs by comparing a variable to specified values.

12

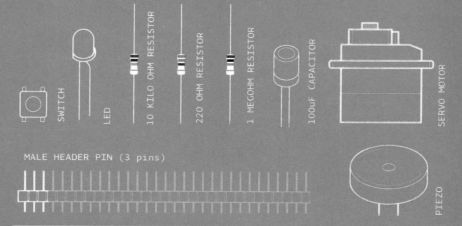

SWITCH

LED

10 KILO OHM RESISTOR

220 OHM RESISTOR

1 MEGOHM RESISTOR

100uF CAPACITOR

SERVO MOTOR

MALE HEADER PIN (3 pins)

PIEZO

INGREDIENTS

KNOCK LOCK

MAKE YOUR OWN SECRET LOCKING MECHANISM TO KEEP UNWANTED GUESTS OUT OF YOUR SPACE!

Discover: input with a piezo, writing your own functions

Time: **1 HOUR**
Level: ■ ■ ■ ■ ■

Builds on projects: **1, 2, 3, 4, 5**

The piezo you used for playing back sounds in the theremin and keyboard projects can also be used as an input device. When plugged into 5V, the sensor can detect vibrations that can be read by the Arduino's analog inputs. You'll need to plug in a high value resistor (like 1-megohm) as the reference to ground for this to work well.

When the piezo is pressed flat against a solid surface that can vibrate, like a wooden table top, your Arduino can sense how intense a knock is. Using this information you can check to see if a number of knocks fall in an acceptable range. In code you can track the number of knocks and see if they match your settings.

A switch will let you lock the motor in place. Some LEDs will give you status: a red LED will indicate the box is locked, a green LED will indicate the box is unlocked, and a yellow LED lets you know if a valid knock has been received.

You'll also be writing your own function that will let you know if a knock is too loud or too soft. Writing your own function helps save time programming by reusing code instead of writing it out many times. Functions can take arguments and return values. In this case, you'll give a function the volume of the knock. If it is in the right range, you'll increment a variable.

It's possible to build the circuit by itself, but it's much more fun if you use this as a tool to lock something. If you have a wooden or a cardboard box you can cut holes into, use the servo motor to open and close a latch, keeping people from getting at your stuff.

BUILD THE
CIRCUIT

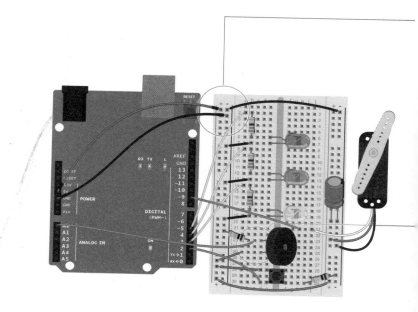

Fig. 1

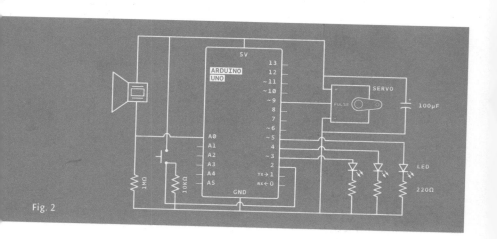

Fig. 2

There is a lot of connections on the board, be sure to keep track of how things are wired up.

1. Connect power and ground to both sides of the breadboard. Place the pushbutton on the breadboard and connect one end to 5V. On the other side of the switch, connect to ground through a 10-kilohm resistor. Connect this junction to digital pin 2 on the Arduino.

2. Attach the wires from the piezo to the breadboard. Attach one wire to power. If your piezo has a red wire or one marked with a "+", that is the one to connect to power. If your piezo doesn't indicate polarity, then you can hook it up either way. Wire the other end of the piezo to Analog Pin 0 on your Arduino. Place a 1-megohm resistor between the ground and the other wire. Lower resistor values will make the piezo less sensitive to vibrations.

3. Wire up the LEDs, connecting the cathodes (short leg) to ground, and placing a 220-ohm resistor in series with the anodes. Through their respective resistors, connect the yellow LED to Arduino digital pin 3, the green LED to digital pin 4, and the red LED to digital pin 5.

4. Insert the male headers into the female socket on the servo motor (see Fig.3). Connect the red wire to power, and the black wire to ground. Place a 100uF electrolytic capacitor across power and ground to smooth out any irregularities in voltage, making sure you have the capacitor's polarity correct. Connect the servo's data wire to pin 9 on your Arduino.

Your servo motor comes with female connectors, so you'll need to add header pins to connect it to the breadboard.
Fig. 3

THE CODE

Servo library

Just as in the earlier Mood Cue Project, you'll need to import the **Servo** library and create an instance to use the motor.

Useful constants

Create constants to name your inputs and outputs.

Variables to hold switch and piezo values

Create variables to hold the values from your switch and piezo.

Knock tresholds

Set up some constants to use as thresholds for the knock maximum and minimum levels.

Variables for lock state and number of knocks

The locked variable will let you know if the lock is enganged or not. A **boolean** is a data type that can only be true (1) or false (0). You should start with the mechanism unlocked.
The last global variable will hold the number of valid knocks you have received.

Setting the direction of the digital pins and initializing servo object and serial port

In your **setup()**, attach the servo to pin 9.
Set the LED pins as outputs and the switch pins as inputs.

Unlock

Initialize serial communication with the computer so you can monitor the knock volume, what the current state of the lock is, and how many more knocks you have to go.
Turn on the green LED, move the servo to the unlocked position, and print the current status to the serial monitor indicating the circuit is in the unlocked position.

Checking the switch

In the **loop()**, you'll first check to see if the box is locked or not. This will determine what happens in the rest of the program. If it is locked, read the switch value.

```
1 #include <Servo.h>
2 Servo myServo;

3 const int piezo = A0;
4 const int switchPin = 2;
5 const int yellowLed = 3;
6 const int greenLed = 4;
7 const int redLed = 5;

8 int knockVal;
9 int switchVal;

10 const int quietKnock = 10;
11 const int loudKnock = 100;

12 boolean locked = false;
13 int numberOfKnocks = 0;

14 void setup(){
15   myServo.attach(9);
16   pinMode(yellowLed, OUTPUT);
17   pinMode(redLed, OUTPUT);
18   pinMode(greenLed, OUTPUT);
19   pinMode(switchPin, INPUT);
20   Serial.begin(9600);

21   digitalWrite(greenLed, HIGH);
22   myServo.write(0);
23   Serial.println("The box is unlocked!");
24 }

25 void loop(){
26   if(locked == false){
27     switchVal = digitalRead(switchPin);
```

Lock

If the switch is closed (you're pressing it), change the locked variable to true, indicating the lock is engaged. Turn the green LED off, and the red LED on. If you don't have the serial monitor on, this is helpful visual feedback to let you know the status of the lock. Move the servo into the lock position, and print out a message to the serial monitor indicating the box is now locked. Add a delay so the lock has plenty of time to move into place.

Checking the knock sensor

If the locked variable is true, and the lock is engaged, read the value of the vibration of the piezo and store it in **knockVal**.

Counting only valid knocks

The next statement checks to see if you have fewer than three valid knocks, and there is some vibration on the sensor. If these are both true, check to see if this current knock is valid or not and increment the **numberOfKnocks** variable. This is where you'll call your custom function **checkForKnocks( )**. You'll write the function once you're finished with the **loop( )**, but you already know you're going to be asking it if this is a valid knock, so pass the knockVal along as an argument. After checking your function, print out the number of knock still needed.

Unlock

Check to see if you have three or more valid knocks. If this is true, change the locked variable to false, and move the servo to the unlocked position. Wait for a few milliseconds to let it start moving, and change the status of the green and red LEDs. Print out a status message to the serial monitor, indicating the box is unlocked.

Close up the **else** statement and the **loop( )** with a pair of curly brackets.

Defining a function to check knock validity

Now it's time to write the function **checkForKnock( )**. When you're writing functions of your own, you need to indicate if it is going to return a value or not. If it is not going to return a value, you declare it as type **void**, similar to the **loop( )** and **setup( )** functions. If it is going to return a value, you must declare what kind (**int**, **long**, **float**, etc.). In this **case**, you're checking to see if a knock is valid (true) or not (false). Declare the function as type boolean.

```
28    if(switchVal == HIGH){
29      locked = true;
30      digitalWrite(greenLed,LOW);
31      digitalWrite(redLed,HIGH);
32      myServo.write(90);
33      Serial.println("The box is locked!");
34      delay (1000);
35    }
36  }
```

```
37  if(locked == true){
38    knockVal = analogRead(piezo);
```

```
39    if(numberOfKnocks < 3 && knockVal > 0){
40      if(checkForKnock(knockVal) == true){
41        numberOfKnocks++;
42      }
43      Serial.print(3-numberOfKnocks);
44      Serial.println(" more knocks to go");
45    }
```

```
46    if(numberOfKnocks >= 3){
47      locked = false;
48      myServo.write(0);
49      delay(20);
50      digitalWrite(greenLed,HIGH);
51      digitalWrite(redLed,LOW);
52      Serial.println("The box is unlocked!");
53    }
54  }
55 }
```

```
56 boolean checkForKnock(int value){
```

This particular function will be checking a number (your variable knockVal) to see if it is valid or not. To pass this variable along to the function, you create a named parameter when you declare the function.

Check validity of knock

In your function, whenever you refer to **value** it will use whatever number it receives as an argument in the main program. At this point **value** will be set to whatever **knockVal** is.
Check to see if **value** is greater than your quiet knock, and less than your loud knock.

Indicating knock is valid

If the value falls between those two values it's a valid knock. Blink the yellow LED once and print the value of the knock to the serial monitor.

Function returns true

To let the main program know what the outcome of the comparison is, you use the command **return**. You use the **return** command, which also terminates the function: once it executes, you return to the main program.

Indicating invalid knock; function returns false

If **value** is either too quiet or too loud, print it out to the serial monitor and return false.

Close up your function with one more bracket .

USE IT

When you first plug in the circuit to your Arduino, open the serial monitor. You should see the green LED turn on, and the servo will move to the unlocked position.

The serial monitor should print out "The box is unlocked!". You'll probably hear the piezo make a small "click" when it first gets power.

Try knocking soft and hard to see what sort of intensity knock triggers your function. You'll know it's working when the yel-

```
57   if(value > quietKnock && value < loudKnock){

58      digitalWrite(yellowLed, HIGH);
59      delay(50);
60      digitalWrite(yellowLed, LOW);
61      Serial.print("Valid knock of value ");
62      Serial.println(value);

63      return true;
64   }

65   else {
66      Serial.print("Bad knock value ");
67      Serial.println(value);
68      return false;
69   }
70 }
```

low LED flashes and the serial monitor tells you you have a valid knock with its value. It will also let you know the number of knocks you have to go before unlocking the box.

Once you've reached the right number of knocks, the red light will turn off, the green light will turn on, the servo will move 90 degrees, and the serial monitor will let you know the lock is disengaged.

The values for your ideal knock may vary from the ones in the example. This depends on a number of different variables, like the type of surface the sensor is attached to and how sturdily it is fixed on there. Using the serial monitor and the AnalogInSerialOut example in the Arduino IDE, find an appropriate knock value for your setup. You can find a detailed explanation of that example here: *arduino.cc/analogtoserial*

If you move the project into a box, you'll need to make holes for the LEDs and the switch. You'll also need to make a latch for the servo motor to spin into. It will probably also be helpful to have a hole to run your USB cable through to find out how sensitive your new environment is to knocks.

You may need to rearrange your breadboard and Arduino, or solder the LEDs and switch to make them accessible to the exterior of your enclosure. Soldering is a process of joining two or more metal components together with an adhesive that is melted between the joint. If you've never soldered before, ask someone who has experience to help you out, or try practicing on some scrap wire before attempting with another device in this project. When you solder something, it's meant to be a permanent connection, so be sure it's something that's ok to hack.

See *arduino.cc/soldering* for a good explanation of how to solder.

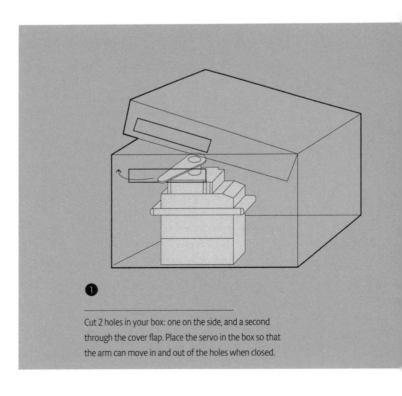

❶

Cut 2 holes in your box: one on the side, and a second
through the cover flap. Place the servo in the box so that
the arm can move in and out of the holes when closed.

Writing your own functions not only allows you to control the flow of your code more easily, it also helps keep it readable as your projects become larger and larger. Over time, as you write more code, you may find you have a large number of functions you can re-use in different projects, making the process quicker and unique to your style of programming.

This example simply counts the right number of knocks, no matter how long it takes. You can start to make a more complex example by creating a timer with `millis()`. Use the timer to identify if the knocks happen in a specific period of time. Look back at the Digital Hourglass Project for an example of how a timer works. You aren't limited to simply finding knocks in a specific range. You can look for complex patterns of knocks based on the amount of vibration and timing together. There are a number of examples online that talk about how to do this, search for "Arduino knock lock" to discover more examples of this type of project.

Piezo elements can be used as inputs when wired up as voltage dividers with a high value resistor. Designing a function is an easy way to write code that can be reused for specific tasks.

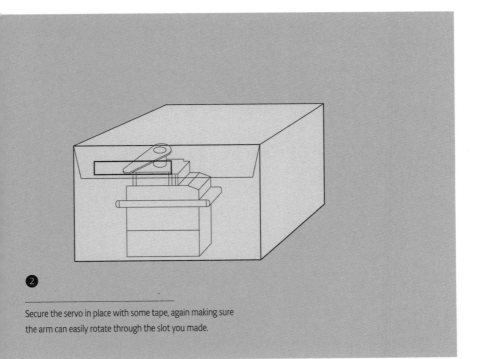

2

Secure the servo in place with some tape, again making sure the arm can easily rotate through the slot you made.

13

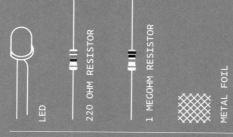

LED

220 OHM RESISTOR

1 MEGOHM RESISTOR

METAL FOIL

INGREDIENTS

TOUCHY-FEELY LAMP

YOU WILL CREATE A LAMP THAT TURNS A LIGHT ON AND OFF WHEN YOU TOUCH A PIECE OF CONDUCTIVE MATERIAL

Discover: installing third party libraries, creating a touch sensor

Time: **45 MINUTES**
Level: ■ ■ ■ ■ ▪

Builds on projects: **1, 2, 5**

You'll be using the CapacitiveSensor library by Paul Badger for this project. This library allows you to measure the capacitance of your body.

Capacitance is a measure of how much electrical charge something can store. The library checks two pins on your Arduino (one is a sender, the other a receiver), and measures the time it takes for them to have the same state. These pins will be connected to a metal object like aluminum foil. As you get closer to the object, your body will absorb some of the charge, causing it to take longer for the two pins to be the same.

Preparing the library

The most recent version of the CapacitiveSensor library is here: *arduino.cc/capacitive* . Download the file to your computer and unzip it. Open your Arduino sketch folder (it will be in your "Documents" folder by default). In the folder, create a new directory named "libraries". Place the CapacitiveSensor folder you unzipped in this folder and restart the Arduino software.
Click the File>Examples menu in the Arduino software, and you'll see a new entry for "CapacitiveSensor". The library you added included an example project. Open the CapacitiveSensorSketch example and compile it. If you don't get any errors, you'll know you installed it correctly.

For more information on libraries:
arduino.cc/en/Reference/Libraries

BUILD THE CIRCUIT

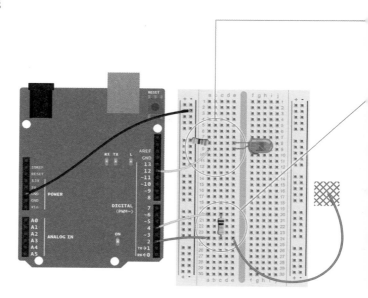

Fig. 1

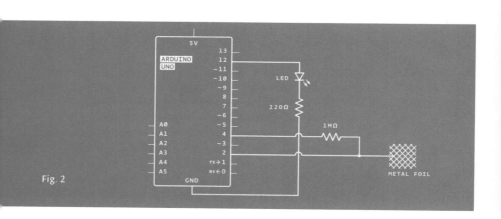

Fig. 2

1. Connect an LED to pin 12, and connect the cathode to ground through a 220-ohm resistor as shown.

2. Connect digital pins 2 and 4 to your breadboard. Connect the two pins with a 1-megahom resistor. In the same row as pin 2, insert a long wire (8-10cm at least) that extends away from the breadboard, not connected to anything on the other end. This will become your touch sensor.

There's no need to supply 5V to your breadboard in this project. Digital pin 4 supplies the current to the sensor.

Just like with other LED projects, diffusing the light will make this much more attractive. Ping pong balls, little lampshades from paper or plastic, whatever you have handy will work.

You can hide the sensor behind something solid and it will still work. Capacitance can be measured through non-conductive materials like wood and plastic. Increasing the surface area of the sensor with a larger conductive surface will make it more sensitve; try connecting aluminum foil, or copper mesh to your wire. You could make a base for the lamp out of cardboard, thin wood, or cloth, and line the inner surface with foil attached to your sensor wire. The whole base of the lamp would then act as a touch sensor. Update the threshold variable in the code when you make these changes to ensure that you're still getting a reliable result.

THE CODE

Import the CapacitiveSensor
library

At the beginning of your program, include the CapacitiveSensor library. You include it the same way you would a native Arduino library like the **Servo** library in the earlier projects.

Create a named instance of the library. When you use this library, you tell the instance what pins it will be using to send and receive information. In this case, pin 4 sends to the conductive sensor material through the resistor, and pin 2 is the sense pin.

Set up the threshold

Set up a variable for the sensing threshold at which the lamp will turn on. You'll change this number after you test the sensor's functionality.

Then define the pin your LED will be on.

In the **setup()** function, open a Serial connection at 9600 bps. You'll use this to see the values the sensor reads. Also, make your ledPin an **OUTPUT**.

Sensing touch

In the **loop()** function, create a variable of type long to hold the sensor's value. The library returns the sensor value using a command called **capacitiveSensor()** that takes an argument identifying the number of samples you want to read. If you read only a few samples, it's possible you'll see a lot of variation in the sensor. If you take too many samples, you could introduce a lag as it reads the sensor multiple times. 30 samples is a good starting value. Print the sensor value to the serial monitor.

Lamp control

With an **if()...else** statement, check to see if the sensor value is higher than the threshold. If it is, turn the LED on. If it is not, turn it off.

Then add a small **delay()** before ending the **loop()**.

```
1 #include <CapacitiveSensor.h>
2 CapacitiveSensor capSensor = CapacitiveSensor(4,2);
```

```
3 int threshold = 1000;
4 const int ledPin = 12;
```

```
5 void setup() {
6   Serial.begin(9600);
7   pinMode(ledPin, OUTPUT);
8 }
```

```
9 void loop() {
10   long sensorValue = capSensor.capacitiveSensor(30);
11   Serial.println(sensorValue);
```

```
12   if(sensorValue > threshold) {
13     digitalWrite(ledPin, HIGH);
14   }
15   else {
16     digitalWrite(ledPin, LOW);
17   }
```

```
18   delay(10);
19 }
```

USE IT

After programming the Arduino, you'll want to find out what the sensor values are when it's touched. Open the serial monitor and note the value coming from the sensor when you're not touching it. Press gently on the bare wire you have exposed from your breadboard. The number should increase. Try pressing more firmly and see if it changes.

Once you have an idea of the range of values you're getting from the sensor, go back to the sketch and change the threshold variable to a number that is greater than the sensor's value when it is not touched, but less than its value when pressed. Upload the sketch with the new value. The light should come on reliably when you touch the wire, and turn off when it's left alone. If you aren't getting the light to turn on, try lowering the threshold a little more.

You probably noticed that the values from the sensor changed depending on how much of your finger was touching the conductor. Can you use this to get other interactions with the LED? What about multiple sensors for fading the light brighter and darker? If you place a different value resistor between pins 2 and 4 it will change the sensitivity. Is this useful for your interface?

Third party libraries like Paul Badger's CapacitiveSensor are useful tools for expanding the capabilities of the Arduino. Once installed, they behave similarly to libraries that are bundled with the core software.

14

POTENTIOMETER

INGREDIENTS

TWEAK THE ARDUINO LOGO

USING SERIAL COMMUNICATION, YOU'LL USE YOUR
ARDUINO TO CONTROL A PROGRAM ON YOUR COMPUTER

Discover: serial communication with a computer program, Processing

Time: **45 MINUTES**

Level: ■ ■ ■ ■ ■

Builds on projects: **1, 2, 3**

You've done a lot of cool stuff with the physical world, now it's time to control your computer with your Arduino. When you program your Arduino, you're opening a connection between the computer and the microcontroller. You can use this connection to send data back and forth to other applications.

The Arduino has a chip that converts the computer's USB-based communication to the serial communication the Arduino uses. Serial communication means that the two computers, your Arduino and PC, are exchanging bits of information serially, or one after another in time.

When communicating serially, computers need to agree on the speed at which they talk to one another. You've probably noticed when using the serial monitor there's a number at the bottom right corner of the window. That number, 9600 bits per second, or baud, is the same as the value you've declared using `Serial.begin()`. That's the speed at which the Arduino and computer exchange data. A bit is the smallest amount of information a computer can understand.

You've used the serial monitor to look at values from the analog inputs; you'll use a similar method to get values into a program you're going to write in a programming environment called **Processing**. Processing is based on Java, and Arduino's programming environment is based on Processing's. They look pretty similar, so you should feel right at home there.

Before getting started with the project, download the latest version of Processing from *processing.org*. It may be helpful to look at the "Getting started" and "Overview" tutorials at *processing.org/learning*. These will help you to familiarize yourself with Processing before you start writing software to communicate with your Arduino.

The most efficient way to send data between the Arduino and Processing is by using the `Serial.write()` function in Arduino. It's similar to the `Serial.print()` function you've been using in that it sends information to an attached computer, but instead of sending human readable information like numbers and letters, it sends values between 0-255 as raw bytes. This limits the values that the Arduino can send, but allows for quick transmission of information.

On both your computer and Arduino, there's something called the serial buffer which holds onto information until it is read by a program. You'll be sending bytes from the Arduino to Processing's serial buffer. Processing will then read the bytes out of the buffer. As the program reads information from the buffer, it clears space for more.

When using serial communication between devices and programs, it's important that both sides not only know how fast they will be communicating, but also what they should be expecting. When you meet someone, you probably expect a "Hello!"; if instead they say something like "The cat is fuzzy", chances are you will be caught off guard. With software, you will need to get both sides to agree on what is sent and received.

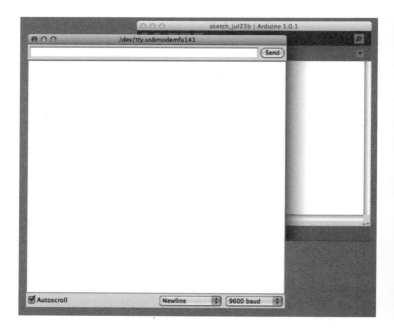

Fig. 1

BUILD THE CIRCUIT

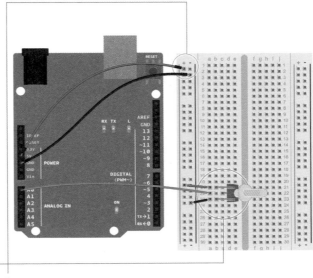

Fig. 2

1 Connect power and ground to your breadboard.

2 Connect each end of your potentiometer to power and ground. Connect the middle leg to analogIn pin 0.

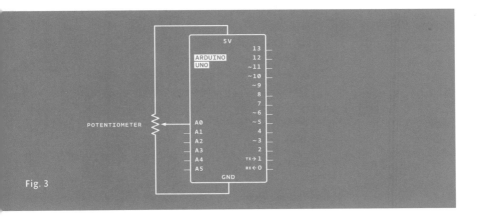

Fig. 3

THE ARDUINO CODE

Open a serial connection

First, program your Arduino. In **setup()**, you'll start serial communication, just as you did earlier when looking at the values from an attached sensor. The Processing program you write will have the same serial baud rate as your Arduino.

Send the sensor value

In the **loop()**, you're going to use the **Serial.write()** command to send information over the serial connection. **Serial.write()** can only send a value between 0 and 255. To make sure you're sending values that fit within that range, divide the analog reading by 4.

Let the ADC stabilize

After sending the byte, wait for one millisecond to let the ADC settle down. Upload the program to the Arduino then set it aside while you write your Processing sketch.

THE PROCESSING CODE

Import the set up the serial object

The Processing language is similar to Arduino, but there are enough differences that you should look at some of their tutorials and the "Getting Started" guide mentioned before to familiarize yourself with the language.

Open a new Processing sketch. Processing, unlike the Arduino, doesn't know about serial ports without including an external library. Import the serial library.

You need to create an instance of the serial object, just like you've done in Arduino with the Servo library. You'll use this uniquely named object whenever you want to use the serial connection.

Create an object for the image

To use images in Processing, you need to create an object that will hold the image and give it a name.

```
1 void setup() {
2    Serial.begin(9600);
3 }
```

```
4 void loop() {
5    Serial.write(analogRead(A0)/4);
```

```
6    delay(1);
7 }
```

**SAVE AND CLOSE
THE ARDUINO IDE
NOW,
LET'S START**

```
1 import processing.serial.*;
2 Serial myPort;
```

```
3 PImage logo;
```

Variable to store the
background color

Create a variable that will hold the background hue of the Arduino logo. The logo is a .png file, and it has built-in transparency, so it's possible to see the background color change.

Processing has a **setup()** function, just like Arduino. Here's where you'll open the serial connection and give the program a couple of parameters that will be used while it runs.

Setting the color mode

You can change the way Processing works with color information. Typically, it works with colors in a Red Green Blue (RGB) fashion. This is similar to the color mixing you did in Project 4, when you used values between 0 and 255 to change the color of an RGB LED. In this program, you're going to use a color mode called HSB, which stands for Hue, Saturation, and Brightness. You'll change the hue when you turn the potentiometer.

colorMode() takes two arguments: the type of mode, and the maximum value it can expect.

Loading the image

To load the Arduino image into the sketch, read it into the logo object you created earlier. When you supply the URL of an image, Processing will download it when you run the program.
With the **size()** function, you tell Processing how large the display window will be. If you use **logo.width** and **logo. height** as the arguments, the sketch will automatically scale to the size of the image you're using.

Printing available serial
ports

Processing has the ability to print out status messages using the **println()** command. If you use this in conjunction with the **Serial.list()** function, you'll get a list of all the serial ports your computer has when the program first starts. You'll use this once you're finished programming to see what port your Arduino is on.

Creating the serial object

You need to tell Processing information about the serial connection. To populate your named serial object **myPort** with the necessary information, the program needs to know it is a new instance of the serial object. The parameters it expects are which application it will be speaking to, which serial port it will communicate over, and at what speed.

```
4 int bgcolor = 0;

5 void setup() {

6   colorMode(HSB, 255);

7   logo = loadImage("http://arduino.cc/logo.png");
8   size(logo.width, logo.height);

9   println("Available serial ports:");
10  println(Serial.list());

11  myPort =
      new Serial(this, Serial.list()[0], 9600);
12 }
```

The attribute **this** tells Processing you're going to use the serial connection in this specific application. The **Serial.list()** **[0]** argument specifies which serial port you're using. **Serial.list()** contains an array of all the attached serial devices. The argument **9600** should look familiar, it defines the speed at which the program will communicate.

The **draw()** function is analogous to Arduino's **loop()** in that it happens over and over again forever. This is where things are drawn to the program's window.

Reading Arduino data from the serial port

Check if there is information from the Arduino. The **myPort.available()** command will tell you if there is something in the serial buffer. If there are bytes there, read the value into the **bgcolor** variable and print it to the debug window.

Setting the image background and displaying the image

The function **background()** sets the color of the window. It takes three arguments. The first argument is the hue, the next is brightness, and the last is saturation. Use the variable bgcolor as the hue value, and set the brightness and saturation to the maximum value, 255.

You'll draw the logo with the command **image()**. You need to tell **image()** what to draw, and what coordinates to start drawing it in the window. 0,0 is the top left, so start there.

USE IT

Connect your Arduino and open the serial monitor. Turn the pot on your breadboard. You should see a number of characters as you twist the knob. The serial monitor expects ASCII characters, not raw bytes. ASCII is information encoded to represent text in computers. What you see in the window is the serial monitor trying to interpret the bytes as ASCII.

When you use **Serial.println()**, you send information formatted for the serial monitor. When you use **Serial.write()**, like in this application you are running now, you're sending raw information. Programs like Processing can understand these raw bytes.

```
13 void draw() {
```

```
14   if (myPort.available() > 0) {
15     bgcolor = myPort.read();
16     println(bgcolor);
17   }
```

```
18   background(bgcolor, 255, 255);
19 image(logo, 0, 0);
20 }
```

Close the serial monitor. Run the Processing sketch by pressing the arrow button in the Processing IDE. Look at the Processing output window. You should see a list similar to the figure below.

This is a list of all the serial ports on your computer. If you're using OSX, look for a string that says something like "/dev/tty.usbmodem411", it will most likely be the first element in the list. On Linux, it may appear as "/dev/ttyUSB0", or similar. For Windows, it will appear as a COM port, the same one you would use when programming the board. The number in front of it is the `Serial.list()[]` array index. Change the number in your Processing sketch to match the correct port on your computer.

Restart the Processing sketch. When the program starts running, turn the potentiometer attached to the Arduino. You should see the color behind the Arduino logo change as you turn the potentiometer. You should also see values printing out in the Processing window. Those numbers correspond to the raw bytes you are sending from the Arduino.

Once you have twisted and turned to your heart's desire, try replacing the pot with an analog sensor. Find something you find interesting to control the color. What does the interaction feel like? It's probably different than using a mouse or keyboard, does it feel natural to you?

When using serial communication, only one application can talk to the Arduino at a time. So if you're running a Processing sketch that is connected to your Arduino, you won't be able to upload a new Arduino sketch or use the serial monitor until you've closed the active application.

With Processing and other programming environments, you can control media on your computer in some remarkable and novel ways. If you're excited about the possibilities of controlling content on your computer, take some time to experiment with Processing. There are several serial communication examples in both the Processing and Arduino IDEs that will help you explore further.

Serial communication enables the Arduino to talk with programs on a computer. Processing is an open source programming environment that the Arduino IDE is based upon. It's possible to control a Processing sketch with the Arduino via serial communication.

15

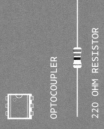

OPTOCOUPLER

220 OHM RESISTOR

INGREDIENTS

HACKING BUTTONS

GET CONTROL OF OTHER COMPONENTS AROUND YOU.
USING SOME ADDITIONAL CIRCUITRY, YOU CAN "PRESS"
BUTTONS WITH YOUR ARDUINO

| Discover: optocoupler, connecting with other components

Time: **45 MINUTES** | Builds on projects: **1, 2, 9**
Level: ■ ■ ■ ■ ■

Warning: You're no longer a beginner if you're doing this project. You'll be opening up an electronic device and modifying it. You'll void your device's warranty, and if you're not careful, you might damage the device. Make sure you're familiar with all the electronics concepts in the earlier projects before you attempt this one. We recommend you use inexpensive items you don't mind damaging for your first few projects, until you develop experience and confidence.

While the Arduino can control a lot of things, sometimes it's easier to use tools that are created for specific purposes. Perhaps you want to control a television or a music player, or drive a remote control car. Most electronic devices have a control panel with buttons, and many of those buttons can be hacked so that you can "press" them with an Arduino. Controlling recorded sound is a good example. If you wanted to record and play back recorded sound, it would take a lot of effort to get the Arduino to do that. It's much easier to get a small device that records and plays back sound, and replace its buttons with outputs controlled by your Arduino.

Optocouplers are integrated circuits that allow you to control one circuit from a different one without any electrical connection between the two. Inside an optocoupler is an LED and a light detector. When the LED in the optocoupler is turned on by your Arduino, the light detector closes a switch internally. The switch is connected to two of the output pins (4 and 5) of the optocoupler. When the internal switch is closed, the two output pins are connected. When the switch is open, they're not connected. This way, it's possible to close switches on other devices without connecting them to your Arduino.

In this example, the diagrams are for controlling a digital recording module that allows you to record and playback 20 seconds of sound, but the basic premise holds for any device that has a switch you can access. While it's possible to use this example without soldering any wires, it certainly makes things easier. For more information on soldering, see p. 134.

BUILD THE CIRCUIT

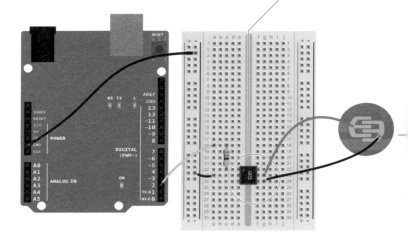

Fig. 1

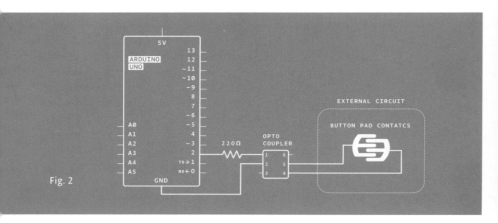

Fig. 2

1. Connect ground to your breadboard through the Arduino.

2. Place the optocoupler on your breadboard so that it straddles the center of the board (see circuit diagram).

3. Connect pin 1 on the optocoupler to Arduino pin 2 in series with a 220-ohm resistor (remember, you're powering an LED inside, you don't want to burn it out). Connect pin 2 of the optocoupler to ground.

4. On the main board of the sound module there is a number of electrical components, including a playback button.
To control the switch, you're going to have to remove the button. Flip the circuit board over and find the tabs that hold the button in place. Gently bend the tabs back and remove the button from the board.

5. Under the button are two small metal plates. This pattern is typical of many electronic devices with pushbuttons. The two "forks" of this pattern are the two sides of the switch. A small metal disc inside the pushbutton connects these two forks when you press the button.

6. When the forks are connected, the switch is closed on the circuit board. You will be closing the switch with the optocoupler.
This method, closing a switch with an optocoupler, works only if one of the two sides of the pushbutton's switch is connected to ground on your device. If you're not sure, take a multimeter and measure the voltage between one of the forks and the ground on your device. You need to do this with the device turned on, so be careful not to touch anywhere else on the board.
Once you know which fork is ground, disconnect the power to your device.

7. Next, connect one wire to each of the small metal plates. If you are soldering these wires, be careful to not join the two sides of the switch together. If you are not soldering and using tape, make sure your connection is secure, or the switch won't close. Make sure neither wire connects to the other fork, or your switch will be closed all the time.

8. Attach the two wires to pins 4 and 5 of the optocoupler. Connect the side of the switch that is grounded to pin 4 of the optocoupler. Connect the other fork to pin 5 of the optocoupler.

THE CODE

Name a constant

Most of the fun with this project is in the circuit and the optocoupler. The code is similar to the first project you made with the Arduino. You're going to play the sound once every 20 seconds by turning pin 2 **HIGH**.

Create a constant for the optocoupler control pin.

Configure the pin direction

In **setup( )**, set the optocoupler pin into an output.

Pull the pin high and low

The **loop( )** turns optoPin **HIGH** for a few milliseconds, long enough for the optocoupler to close the switch on the device. Then the optoPin becomes **LOW**.

Wait for a little while

Wait for 21 seconds for the whole message to play back before starting the **loop( )** again.

USE IT

Attach the battery to the sound recorder. Press and hold the record button on the device. While you're holding the button, you can record audio into the microphone. Use your voice, the cat, or the pots and pans in the kitchen to make some noise (but be careful with the cat).

Once you've satisfactorily recorded a sound, power your Arduino with the USB cable. Your recording should start to play. If you recorded for the full 20 seconds, the sound should start again just a few moments after it ends.

Try experimenting with different sounds and durations of toggling the playback with the **delay( )** in your program.

If you trigger the switch while a sound is playing, it will stop. How can you take advantage of this to create unique sequences of sounds?

```
1  const int optoPin = 2;

2  void setup(){
3    pinMode(optoPin, OUTPUT);
4  }

5  void loop(){
6    digitalWrite(optoPin, HIGH);
7    delay(15);
8    digitalWrite(optoPin, LOW);

9    delay(21000);
10 }
```

Integrated circuits are in virtually every electronic device. The large 28 pin chip on your Arduino is an IC that houses the brains of the board. There are other ICs that support this one with communication and power. The optocoupler and main chip on the Arduino are *Dual In-line Package (DIP)* chips. These DIP chips are the kind that most hobbyists use because they easily fit in a breadboard and don't have to be permanently soldered to be used.

The project example only played sound back at a regular interval. How could you incorporate the inputs from earlier projects to trigger these sounds? What other battery powered things do you have around the house that need an Arduino to control them? This technique of controlling an electronic device with an optocoupler by connecting to the two sides of a switch can be used in many other devices. What other devices do you want to control?

Optocouplers can control devices that are on a different circuit. The two circuits are electrically separated from each other inside the component.

A/Z

Accelerometer -
Actuator -
Alternating current -
Amperage (amps or amperes) -
Analog -
Analog-to-Digital Converter (ADC) -
Anode -
Argument -
Array -
Back-voltage -
Baud -
Binary -
Bit -
Boolean -
Byte -
Calibration -
Capacitance -
Cathode -
Circuit -
Common cathode LED -
Conductor -
Constant -
Current -
Datasheet -
Datatype -
Debugging -
Decoupling capacitors -
Digital -
Direct current -

Drain (transistor) -
Dual In-line Package (DIP) -
Duty cycle -
Electricity -
Float -
Function -
Gate -
Global variable -
Ground -
IDE -
Index -
Induction -
Instance -
Insulator -
Int -
Integrated Circuit (IC)-
Library -
Load -
Local variable -
Long -
Microcontroller -
Millisecond -
Object -
Ohm -
Ohm's Law -
Optocoupler -
Parallel -
Parameter -
Period -
Photocell -

Photoresistor -
Phototransistor -
Polarized -
Power supply -
Processing -
Pseudocode -
Pulse Width Modulation (PWM) -
Resistance -
Sensor -
Serial buffer -
Serial communication -
Serial monitor -
Series -
Short circuit -
Sketch -
Soldering -
Source (transistor) -
Square wave -
Switch -
Transducer -
Transistor -
Unsigned -
USB -
Variable -
Voltage -
Voltage divider -

GLOSSARY

THERE ARE A NUMBER OF NEW TERMS
YOU'VE LEARNED IN THESE PROJECTS.
WE'VE COLLECTED THEM ALL HERE FOR
REFERENCE

Accelerometer - A sensor that measures acceleration. Sometimes, they are used to detect orientation, or tilt.

Actuator - A type of component that changes electrical energy into motion. Motors are a type of actuator.

Alternating current - A type of current where electricity changes its direction periodically. This is the sort of electricity that comes out of a wall socket.

Amperage (amps or amperes) - The amount of electrical charge flowing past a specific point in your circuit. Describes the current as it flows through a conductor, like a wire.

Analog - Something that can continuously vary over time.

Analog-to-Digital Converter (ADC) - A circuit that converts an analog voltage into a digital number representing that voltage. This circuit is built-in to the microcontroller, and is connected to the analog input pins A0-A5. Converting an analog voltage into a digital number takes a tiny bit of time, so we always follow the analogRead() with a short delay().

Anode - The positive end of a capacitor or diode (remember that an LED is a type of diode).

Argument - A type of data supplied to a function as an input. For example, for digitalRead() to know what pin to check, it takes an argument in the form of a pin number.

Array - In programming, this is a group of variables that are identified by one name, and accessed by an index number.

Back-voltage - Voltage that pushes back against the current that created it. It can be created by motors spinning down. This can damage circuits, which is why diodes are often used in conjunction with motors.

Baud - Shorthand for "bits per second", signifying the speed at which computers are communicating with each other.

Binary - A system with only two states, like true/false or off/on.

Bit - The smallest piece of information a computer can send or receive. It has two states, 0 and 1.

Boolean - A datatype that indicates if something is true or false.

Byte - 8 bits of information. A byte can hold a number between 0 and 255.

Calibration - The process of making adjustments to certain numbers or components to get the best results from a circuit or program. In Arduino projects, this is often used when sensors in the real world may give different values in different circumstances, for instance the amount of light on a photoresistor. Calibration can be automatic, as in Project 6, or manual, as in Project 3.

Capacitance - The ability of something to hold an electrical charge. This charge can be measured with the Capacitive Sensor library, as seen in Project 13.

Cathode - The end of a capacitor or diode that typically connects to ground.

Circuit - A circular path from a power supply, through a load, and then back again to the other end of the power supply. Current flows in a circuit only if it is closed, that is, if the outgoing and return path are both uninterrupted, or closed. If either path is interrupted, or open, then current will not flow through the circuit.

Common cathode LED - Types of LEDs that have multiple colors in one fixture, with one cathode and multiple anodes.

Conductor - Something that enables electricity to flow, like a wire.

Constant - A named identifier that cannot change its value in a program.

Current - The flow of electrical charge through a closed circuit. Measured in amps.

Datasheet - A document written by engineers for other engineers that describes the design and functionality of electrical components. Typical information in a datasheet includes the maximum voltage and current a component requires, as well as an explanation of the functionality of the pins.

Datatype - A classification system that determines what values a particular constant, variable, or array will hold. Int, float, long and boolean are all types that can be used in Arduino.

Debugging - The process of going through a circuit or code, and finding errors (also referred as "bugs"), until the expected behavior is achieved.

Decoupling capacitors - Capacitors that are used to regulate spikes and dips in voltage, often placed close to a sensor or actuator.

Digital - A system of discrete values. As Arduino

is a type of digital device, it only knows of two discrete states, off and on, nothing in between.

Direct current - A type of current which always flows in the same direction. All the projects in this kit use direct current.

Drain (transistor) - The pin that connects to the higher current/voltage load to be controlled.

Dual In-line Package (DIP) - A type of packaging for integrated circuits that allows the components to be easily inserted into a breadboard.

Duty cycle - A ratio indicating the amount of time over a certain period that a component is turned on. When using a PWM value of 127 (out of a total of 256), you're creating a 50% duty cycle.

Electricity - A type of energy generated by electric charges. You can use electronic components to change electricity to other forms of energy, like light and heat.

Float - A datatype that can be expressed as a fraction. This entails the use of decimal points for floating point numbers.

Function - A block of code that executes a specific task repeatedly.

Gate - The pin on a transistor that is connected to the Arduino. When the gate is turned on,

by applying 5V, it closes the junction between drain and source, completing the circuit it is connected to.

Global variable - A named variable that can be accessed anywhere inside your program. It is declared before the setup() function.

Ground - The point of a circuit where there is 0 potential electrical energy. Without a ground, electricity will not have a place to flow in a circuit.

IDE - Stands for "Integrated Development Environment". The Arduino IDE is the place where you write software to upload to the Arduino. It contains all the functions the Arduino can understand. Other programming environments, like Processing, have their own IDE.

Index - The number supplied to an array that indicates which element you're referring to. Computers are zero-indexed, which means they start counting at 0 instead of 1. To access the third element in an array named tones, for example, you would write tones[2].

Induction - The process of using electrical energy to create a magnetic field. This is used in motors to spin them around.

Instance - A copy of a software object. You're using instances of the Servo library in Projects 5 and 12, in each case, you're creating a named instance of the Servo library to use in the project.

Insulator - Something that prevents electricity from flowing. Conductive materials like wires are often covered in insulators like rubber.

Int - A datatype that holds a whole number between −32,768 and 32,767.

Integrated Circuit (IC) - A circuit that has been created on a tiny piece of silicon and embedded in plastic (or epoxy). Pins, or legs, protruding from the body allow you to interact with the circuit inside. Very often we can make good use of an IC knowing only what to connect to the pins without having to understand how it functions internally.

Library - A piece of code that expands the functionality of a program. In the case of Arduino libraries, they either enable communication with a particular piece of hardware, or are used for manipulating data.

Load - A device that turns electrical energy into something else, such as light, heat, or sound.

Local variable - A type of variable that is used for a short amount of time, then forgotten. A variable declared inside the setup() of a program would be local: after the setup() finished running, the Arduino would forget that the variable ever existed.

Long - A datatype that can hold a very large number, from –2,147,483,648 to 2,147,483,647.

Microcontroller - The brains of the Arduino, this is a small computer that you will program to listen for, process, and display information.

Millisecond - 1/1,000th of a second. The Arduino goes through its programs so fast, when calling delay() and other time based functions, it's done in milliseconds.

Object - An instance of a library. When using the Servo library, were you to create an instance named myServo, myServo would be the object.

Ohm - Unit of measurement of resistance. Represented by the omega symbol (Ω).

Ohm's Law - A mathematical equation that demonstrates the relationship between resistance, current and voltage. Usually stated as V (voltage) = I (current) x R (resistance).

Optocoupler - Also known as an opto-isolator, photo-coupler, photo-isolator, photo-switch, and opto-switch. An LED is combined in a sealed case with a phototransistor. The LED is positioned to illuminate the phototransistor, so that when the LED is turned on, the phototransistor will conduct. Used to provide a high degree of isolation as there is no electrical connection common to the input and the output.

Parallel - Components connected across the same two points in a circuit are in parallel. Parallel components always have the same voltage drop across them.

Parameter - When declaring a function, a named parameter serves as the bridge between the local variables in the function, and the arguments it receives when the function is called.

Period - A specific span of time in which something happens. When the period changes, you're adjusting the frequency at which something will occur.

Photocell - A device for converting light energy to electrical energy.

Photoresistor - A resistive device whose resistance varies according to how much light falls on it.

Phototransistor - A transistor which is controlled by light rather than by current.

Polarized - The leads of polarized components (e.g. LEDs or capacitors) have different functions, and thus must be connected the right way. Polarized components connected the wrong way might not work, might be damaged, or might damage other parts of your circuit. Non-polarized components (e.g. resistors) can be connected either way.

Power supply - A source of energy, usually a battery, transformer, or even the USB port of your computer. Comes in many varieties such as regulated or unregulated, AC or DC. Usually the voltage is specified, along with the maximum current the supply can deliver before failing.

Processing - A programming environment based on the Java language. Used as a tool to introduce people to the concepts of programming, and in production environments. The Arduino IDE is written in Processing, and so will look very familiar. In addition, Processing and Arduino share a similar philosophy and motive, of creating free open source tools allowing non-technical people to work with hardware and software.

Pseudocode - A bridge between writing in a computer programming language and using natural speech. When creating pseudocode, it's helpful to write in short declarative statements.

Pulse Width Modulation (PWM) - A way to

simulate an analog output when using a digital device, PWM involves turning a pin on and off at a very rapid rate. The ratio of ON time to OFF time determines the simulated analog result.

Resistance - A measure of how efficiently a material will conduct electricity. In particular, resistance can be calculated by Ohm's Law as: R = V/I.

Sensor - A component that measures one form of energy (like light or heat or mechanical energy) and converts it to electrical energy, which the Arduino can understand.

Serial buffer - A place in your computer's and microcontroller's memory where information received in serial communication is stored until it is read by a program.

Serial communication - The means by which the Arduino communicates with computers and other devices. It involves sending one bit of information at a time in a sequential order. The Arduino has a USB-to-serial converter onboard, which enables it to talk with devices that don't have a dedicated serial port.

Serial monitor - A tool built in to the Arduino IDE allowing sending and receiving serial data to and from a connected Arduino. See the Serial() set of functions.

Series - Components are in series when current flows from the first into the next. The current flowing through both is the same, and the voltage drops across each component.

Short circuit - A short circuit between power and ground will make your circuit stop working and thus should be avoided. In some cases this might damage your power supply or parts of your circuit, and rare cases might start a fire.

Sketch - The term given to programs written in the Arduino IDE.

Soldering - The process of making an electrical connection by melting solder over electrical components or wires that are to be connected. This provides a solid connection between components.

Source (transistor) - The pin on a transistor that connects to ground. When the gate receives power, the source and drain are connected, completing the circuit that is being controlled.

Square wave - A type of waveform that is identified by having only two states, on and off. When used to generate tones, they can sound "buzzy".

Switch - A component that can open or close an electrical circuit. There are many different kinds of switches; the ones in the kit are momentary meaning, they only close the circuit while being pressed.

Transducer - Something that changes one form of energy into another.

Transistor - A 3 terminal (usually) electronic device which can act as either an amplifier or a switch. A control voltage or current between two leads controls a (usually) higher voltage or current between a different pair of leads. Common types of transistors include the Bipolar Junction Transistor (BJT) and the Metal Oxide Semiconductor Field Effect Transistor (MOSFET). Often used to allow a small current from an Arduino (limited to 40 mA) to control substantially larger currents, such as those needed by motors, relays, or incandescent lamps. Depending on how they are constructed, transistors are either N-channel or P-channel, which determines how they should be connected.

Unsigned - A term used to describe some datatypes, indicating that they cannot be a negative number. It's helpful to have an unsigned number if you only need to count in one direction. For instance, when keeping track of time with millis(), it's advisable to use the unsigned long datatype.

USB - Stands for Universal Serial Bus. It's a generic port that is standard on most computers today. With a USB cable, it's possible to program and power an Arduino over a USB connection.

Variable - A place in your computer's or microcontroller's memory for storing information needed in a program. Variables store values which are likely to change as your program runs. A variable's type depends on the type of information you want to store, and the maximum size of the information; for example, a byte can store up to 256 different values, but an int can store up t 65,536 different values. Variables can be local to a particular block of code, or global to an entire program. (see Global variable, Local variable).

Voltage - A measure of potential energy, that

a charge might be pushed with if provided a closed circuit.

Voltage divider - A type of circuit that provides an output that is a fraction of its input voltage. You are building a voltage divider when you combine a photoresistor with a fixed resistor to provide an analog input. A potentiometer is another example of a voltage divider.

FURTHER READING

Getting Started with Arduino by **Massimo Banzi** [O'Reilly Media / Make, 2011]. The definitive introduction to Arduino.

Getting Started with Processing by **Casey Reas** and **Ben Fry** [O'Reilly Media / Make, 2010]. This short guide to the Processing programming environment tells you more about how to program graphics, sounds, and multimedia on your computer.

Making Things Talk, 2nd Edition by **Tom Igoe** [O'Reilly Media / Make, 2011]. Written for more experienced Arduino users, this book gives you many techniques for communicating between Arduino microcontrollers and other devices on the internet, and beyond.

Learning Processing: A Beginner's Guide to Programming Images, Animation, and Interaction by **Daniel Shiffman** [Morgan Kaufman, 2009]. An in-depth introduction to programming using Processing, for beginners of all ages.

Getting Started with RFID by **Tom Igoe** [O'Reilly Media / Make, 2012]. A short introduction to using Radio Frequency Identification with Arduino and Processing.

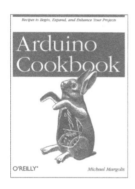

The Arduino Cookbook, 2nd Edition by **Michael Margolis** [O'Reilly Media / Make, 2011]. This book has a lot of great recipes for how to use Arduino in more advanced ways.

Making Things Move: DIY Mechanisms for Inventors, Hobbyists, and Artists by **Dustyn Roberts** [McGraw-Hill, 2010]. A great resource on building movable mechanisms to interface with your projects.

Make: Electronics, by **Charles Platt** [O'Reilly Media / Make, 2009]. Cleverly written introduction to electronics suitable for just about anyone. No Arduinos were used in the making of this book, but it's a valuable text to understand electronics better.

iOS Sensor Apps with Arduino, by **Alasdair Allan** [O'Reilly Media / Make, 2011]. With this concise guide, you'll learn how to connect an external sensor to an iOS device and have them talk to each other through Arduino. You'll also build an iOS application that will parse the sensor values it receives and plot the resulting measurements, all in real-time.

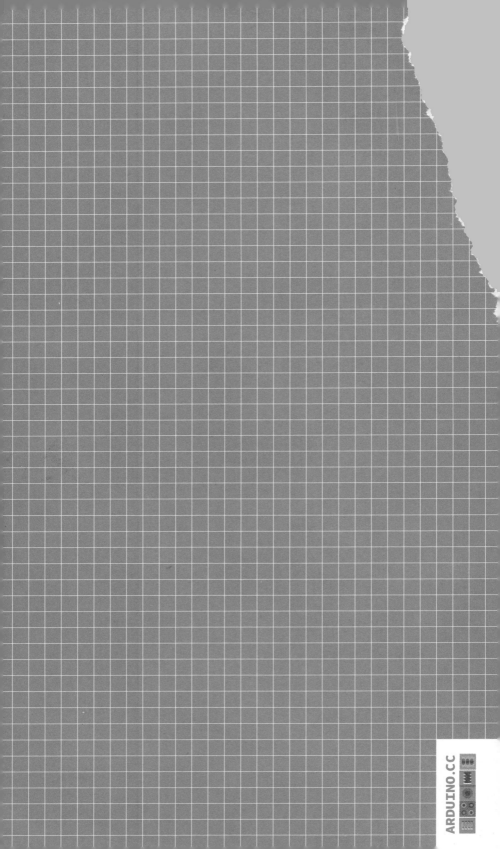